Between the Leaves

Between the Leaves

A Gathering of Writings by Booksellers

Edited by Stuart Miller

Net proceeds from the sale of this book will be donated to First Book, a nonprofit organization that gives disadvantaged children a first book of their own.

This edition published by Barnes & Noble, Inc.

1998 Barnes & Noble Books

Text design by Nicola Ferguson

ISBN 0-7607-0936-X

Printed and bound in the United States of America

98 99 00 01 02 03 M 9 8 7 6 5 4 3 2 1

BVG

Contents

Illustrations

Introduction

It is the bookseller's job, and very often his or her pleasure, to take part in offering the best of the written word to the reading public. But what about words written by the booksellers themselves? The image of the bookstore employee as artist is a familiar one in our popular culture. Movies make use of—and sometimes, unfortunately, fun of—the bespectacled sales clerk who is working on a novel in the evenings. But it is not only an image. The fact is, many of our best writers have careers in bookselling behind them. (Admittedly, *way* behind them.) Be that as it may, nowadays the bookseller's novel- or poem-in-progress is just as likely to get worked on in the daytime. Some bookstores, you see, are open until midnight.

Barnes & Noble is pleased to present in these pages the work of some of those booksellers among us who write, and draw, with serious dedication. It is not a definitive collection, because there are many good writers working here whom we were not able to include in the space allotted. I think, though, that it is a representative one in several respects: It includes the work of both men and women; of the relatively young and those for whom bookselling is a "second career"; and it includes writers and artists from all sections of the country (yes, even Hawaii) and at every level of job description. The contributors, however, are not all out there in the bookstores. A few of them work in the corporate offices.

As for the variety of works, there are humorous stories and serious ones; works one could only describe as "eloquent," others that must be labeled "raw." There's a science fiction thriller and a historical "period" tale. And there are dozens of poems, narrative and lyrical. There's also a wide range of styles and techniques at work. Some poets are formalists—many submitted sonnets, ballads, or haiku. Even more write free verse. One or two writers appear to have invented their own forms—and stuck to them. In addition to works solidly grounded in the tradition of realism, there are poems and stories of ethereal—dare I say "flaky"?—appeal. Some stories are told almost entirely in dialogue; in others, the narrator's voice is never broken—or even disturbed—by the intrusion of characters. There are modernist and postmodern experiments. There are also several works of nonfiction in the form of short personal essays. And we've included what are, to my mind, some gracefully executed black-and-white line drawings that enhance the book.

The main criteria for deciding *what* to include were few. The writing or drawing had to be clear and strong, and to convince by the clarity of its voice and the authority of its craftsmanship. Personal recollections, however heartfelt, had to be judged by the vitality of the writing, and not simply by the underlying emotion. Originality, too, was considered a plus, but had to be accompanied by commensurate skill.

The kind of work—meaning "content" or "style"—was not an issue. There was no impulse to choose stories with an optimistic viewpoint over "downers," or to prefer personal poems to those with a political edge. Or vice versa. Nor was there any attempt to select works composed in conventional English rather than those rooted in slang or dialect. "Is it good in terms of what it sets out to do?" was our primary question. Large, ambitious offerings—while admirable—were not assumed to be more intrinsically valuable than small, careful work. Whatever was most fully achieved is what held our interest.

As to *whose* work was accepted, that was an easier process from which to filter out any devilish preconceptions. The name and address of each author was removed from the submitted pages before being reviewed. The works were then read by several people and evaluated. Where there were disagreements about inclusion, I made the decision. Only after the final decisions were made were the names of the authors revealed. It was a happy event to see how broadly representative our final choices were. Happy, but not very surprising, since it confirmed what we already knew: Talent is randomly distributed, demographically speaking.

We hope this anthology will be of interest to all readers who want to keep abreast of recent works of imagination. We particularly like to suppose that booksellers have a special mission, to which creative ability is, if not exactly an aid, at least a delightful adjunct. Whatever the case, perhaps the next time you enter a bookstore and see an employee with a furrowed brow, you may allow yourself to wonder if she's weeding a rough patch of dialogue, or he's worrying over a rhyme.

—Stuart Miller
1998

Special thanks to Carol Kelly-Gangi for her help in reading and reviewing submitted material. And a special salute to the late Alan Walker, who, sadly, is unable to see his work in print.

Between the Leaves

DAN BENTLEY-BAKER

Anselmo's Boat

Every day of his ninety-fourth year, Anselmo worked on his boat; his last boat, he admitted, and his last year. He had come from Cuba in a boat with his father when fishermen and spongers called in at Tampa and Key West, never Miami, because the town was then just a settlement of New Englanders and Bahamians with little to attract working men. Anselmo was only a small boy then. Smooth and bright in the eyes, and dark stained by the sun, but always looking this way and that, always finding the shoals of anchovetas before any of the men. *Allá, papi,* he would call, pointing over the bows and leaning out over the water like a terrier with the scent of wild hens. He saw the gulls and knew. *Papi, a derecha* in his high, clear voice. The gulls would answer. There was enough for them all.

Now, in his ninety-fourth summer, Anselmo was thick and slow. Upon waking each morning, as he had always done he would take a communion cup of aged rum and cross himself before the tall oak dresser which his wife had left him. She always set out his necessities: his cup, his mirror, and rosary upon a linen napkin which her mother had crocheted in Spain. Anselmo took his silver cup of *añejo* and crossed himself before her picture, which stood in place of the mirror, and left the rosary for her upon the graying, decaying linen napkin. *Espiritu santi.* Ninety-four years, because she came in another boat and had lived long. They had always loved. Here she was in her confirmation dress, and here in a pair of red shorts, small and dark like him, playing with crabs while their fathers cut fish and smoked Monte Cristos because the boats were full. And here she was in her wedding gown, with the fine mantilla of Andalusian lace. On the dresser which she left.

Wearing his habitual khaki shorts and little else, just a pair of rubber thongs for his feet and a pelt of white hair on his chest, Anselmo let himself out of the house quietly so as not to disturb his granddaughter and her son in their room, and stepped across the broken flagstones to his workshop. He greeted old Serbero, an ancient short-legged hound of international lineage who lived in the shop, and lifted his eyes just briefly to the upturned boat resting on cradles, dominating the workroom like a sleeping elephant. Satisfied the boat was as he had left it the night before, Anselmo stepped to the workbench and fed old Serbero dry food from a bag on the table next to a spool of jute cordage. He lifted a plate from a gallon tin and poured the dog some fresh water, then filled the coffeemaker from the same tin and went on preparing his morning *colada*.

Serbero led his master to the big doors and hobbled around in anticipation. Anselmo pushed open the tall green doors and gave the dog his morning run. The sun was sitting brilliant and silver on the horizon, the light sharp as broken glass across the flat sea. The heat suffused Anselmo's face and chest immediately with unhesitating energy so commanding, so strong. In his youth, all the men dared the sun and defied the sea. They all felt invincible, took their invincibility from the sea and the sun. Their bodies were as hard and unyielding then. Most were gone. But the sun was not. The sea was not.

The touch of coolness the night had left was instantly dispelled when the odors opened in the morning. The little mangrove cay about a hundred yards out to the left harbored flocks of egrets and cormorants, who were resting at this hour after probing for a bite at dawn. They hid in the shade and flapped their gullets already like panting dogs. The heat of the sun came so quickly and stayed so long in summer.

Serbero came back with his head held low and tail wagging. He carried a coconut husk in his mouth.

"*Ay, viejo, un regalo, sí,*" Anselmo sang low and sweetly for the old dog. He touched his head and lifted his muzzle, taking the husk as if it were a cock pheasant. "*Muy bien, amigo mío.*" Serbero got down to his belly, front legs and then hind legs and rested his head on the concrete. Anselmo placed the coconut husk on his workbench and poured himself a dram of *café. Espiritu santi, café y el sol.* They had always loved. The coffee and the sun brought out the first sweat. Cuban air-conditioning. The invincible spirits. *In nomine Patri e Filio e'Spiritu Santi café y sol.* Amen.

Anselmo's friend hailed him from the flagstones. "Anselmo, good morning, eh?"

He was a young American who had become interested in the boat. Anselmo turned to greet him. Serbero growled and then wagged. "Gonna be a hot one," the American said.

"Yes, yes," Anselmo said. "They are all hot ones, my friend. Hot ones, *sí,* Biro. Come in, come in."

Anselmo and his American friend drank coffee. The young man's name was Virgil but this was difficult for Anselmo to say so it became Biro, which the young man liked.

"I see you paid the devil last night," Biro said, looking at the long curved hull.

Anselmo narrowed his eyes and looked at the man's face. *"Qué dije?"*

Biro looked over at Anselmo and laughed. "The lar-board strake. That's what Yankees call the last plank before the keel."

He stepped over to the boat and ran his hand along the curved kelson and the thick plank running along it. "The devil board, because it's the one that curves the most, I guess. And it has to be perfect. I see you tamped in the last strip of flax by the devil last night."

Anselmo laughed. "We call it *'la penga china,'* " he said, holding up his crooked index finger. They both laughed.

Anselmo made the poking gesture with his hand and finger. *"Como la viuda anoche,"* he said, making the ob-scene gesture. His eyes sparkled. "Last night I make the widow sing. *Bumba, bumba,* like this."

The men laughed. For two days they had been at the boat with rawhide mallets and broad, flat chisels tamping the flaxen rope into the chinks between the planks. *Tap, bump-bump-bump tap.* The repetition taking on a complex rhythm between the two of them, a meditation in unison, then in counterpoint. *Bumba, bumba.* Like a merengue or a crippled samba. Biro, the tall American in his thirties, showed a bead of sweat on his temples. The day was going to be a hot one.

Anselmo's granddaughter brought out sweet rolls at eight-thirty and replaced the tin of fresh water from a por-celain pitcher. Her son, Nicolas, who was eight years old, stayed and watched the men working even though the pitch stung his eyes. Nicolas leaned on the workbench and held his head in his palm, wiping his eyes occasionally as An-selmo and Biro slathered on resinous black pitch from a wooden cask. The boy watched them work on opposite sides of the twelve-foot boat, swaying with their efforts this way and that, down the sides of the boat. They used the edge of the coarse brushes to work the pine tar pitch into the cracks and soak the flaxen caulking. Then swept the boards in long, pulling motions to smooth the black sealer into the grain of the wood. When they were done, it was time for lunch and siesta, even though little Nicolas had long since fallen asleep with the dog on a pile of sails and rope.

Biro clapped Anselmo on the shoulder and walked off for home. Anselmo took a sip of rum from a bottle of Matusalem on his workbench and cleared his nose in the sand. The sun was high and an armada of cumulus clouds was advancing across the Florida Straits, where the sun had risen hours before. His back and arms were covered with a layer of oily sweat, the constant evaporation of which had kept him cool. He splashed himself with some of the fresh water that Angela had brought out and drank from the can, allowing a cooling rivulet to spill out at the corners of his mouth and cascade down his neck and chest. Serbero lapped and stroked the old man's feet without haste.

The sun glowed like flame on her shoulders and breasts, so small and soft, so brown. Her hair was tangled and stiff in the saltwater. It shaded her eyes and neck. Matilda Maria de Acosta y Ruiz. Just a baby like him. Sitting in the shallow water where the sand was white as sugar and the sea looked like a mirror stretching out across the Florida Bay. Their fathers smoked cigars and laughed, broke into pieces of songs, and tossed the gutted and scaled *rojada* into barrels of salt.

I will love you always. The sun burned fiercely on his back and neck, the water stung his hands where he had handled the fish. For his papi, for her. Her eyes reflected the flat sea and sky like a vision in a crystal ball. She could see the green and blue and white. She could see the boy. I will love you always.

In the late afternoon, after they had eaten a fish soup and cornbread and iced red wine, after siesta, Anselmo went back to his workshop and met Biro once again.

"What will you name her?" Biro said.

Anselmo frowned. *"Qué?"*

"The boat. What will you name the boat. She's almost finished."

Anselmo looked at his feet and scratched his neck. "It is a work boat. You don't name a work boat, *señor*. A number, if you register it with the state, but a name. I don't know."

Biro kept his superstitions to himself. It was Anselmo's boat.

Finding the pitch still tacky, which it would continue to be because of the weather, the men decided to move the boat out into the sun. It took several hours to collect enough men to lift and maneuver the heavy wooden craft the few yards down the beach for this purpose. But in the end, it was a happy occasion. They decided to right the boat and launch it. At least, to set it into the water so the pitch would harden and cool. Then little Nicolas gaped as the men bailed water into the boat and sprinkled rum on the stem post and thwarts.

"Grandpa, why are they doing that? It's your boat, it's not right."

Anselmo smiled and gripped the boy's shoulder gently. "The saltwater inside the boat will make the flax expand and press against the wood. It is necessary. A new boat will leak if it is dry."

Nicolas stared, unused to the irony. Anselmo watched the boy's eyes.

"And the rum is for Chango, the Trickster, so he will like the boat and not be jealous."

"Chango?"

"*Sí. El hijo del Poseidón. Conoces?* God of the sea."

Nicolas stared at the boat. The men smoked cigars and took some of Chango's offering internally, lest they be lost at sea.

Between five and six it rained. The armada having made landfall. And when the last of them had rolled over the island and began again drawing moisture from Florida Bay and the gulf beyond, enough of the humidity had been blanched from the air to break the heat and cool the afternoon. The herons and egrets began stalking the flats again and the old-time Conchs of Matacumbe Key breathed easy. Bonefish guides returned across the flats with tourist fishermen in the bows; housewives and mothers came out to walk along the lanes under mahoes and sabal palms. Even men forced to wear ties and women in panty hose found a way to look out across the western channels and let some of the first onshore breeze brush against their faces.

"This is the longest day, Grandpa," Nicolas said at supper.

"Cómo?"

"Yes, *Abuelo,*" Angela said. She put a plate of sweet plantains on the table. "The summer soltice, is that it? The longest day of the year. Believe it, eh?"

"Summer solstice," Nicolas said, echoing what he had heard on the television. "Longest day of the year."

It was not easy to sleep. A steady movement of air came across the windowsill, a constant flow. With just enough force to break through the screen. Anslemo rested on his bed atop the sheets, wearing nothing but a pair of clean cotton shorts. It was not the heat. The air moved enough to enliven the *mosquitero* hanging in gathered shrouds at the foot of the bed. It was their bed, the bed they bought when they got married. That was the day he signed up to fight the Kaiser. The Kaiser. The bed was built like a boat. Built of Honduran mahogany with cypress pegs, each tall post carved from a single beam and tapered gracefully into a canopy of gossamer-thin netting. Their children had been conceived and born in this bed. Matilda Maria de Acosta y Ruiz had breathed her last breath on earth in this bed. An old woman. A long life. Always loved.

What do you name the boat. Every boat he ever made had the same name. Like the bed. Everything he ever owned bore the same name. Everything he would ever have.

Anselmo rolled and sat up on the side of the bed. Strong, cool moonlight illuminated the room with remarkable brilliance. He could see every feature of molding and every piece of furniture. The room was a monochrome in pale blue and deep blue, with accents in dark indigo and black. He edged forward and put his feet into the square of bright moonlight cast upon the floor and expected his soles to touch water. The floor was cool and he stood up, felt himself buoyed up, as if supported by still, cool water.

Everything he owned. He picked up a silver brush. Everything he touched. The cup, the rosary, the napkin, the dresser, the hands which held these things. All the same. Invincible.

The tide had come up and lifted the boat, which was moored loosely to the concrete dock. Outside, the moonlight burned so bright. He could see his fingernails and his ring. He could see the little waves lapping at the edge of the concrete slab. The sky was a bright pewter, a clear pearl. Three solitary clouds high overhead glistened in borders of silver white as white as a welder's torch. Three clouds. *Reyes magos* on the shortest night of the longest day. Three ships, three kings, a trinity of all things. She was in the shallow water where the moonlight illuminated the sand so white and her eyes were hidden beneath her hair. In the fine mantilla of Andalusian lace. All things which carried one name.

The sound of the dog's whimpering attracted Anselmo's attention to the workshop. He pushed open one heavy door and found the dog on its side looking up.

"Serbero, *fidelio*."

Serbero looked ashamed, as if chastised by his balky legs, as if betraying his master with his infirmity. Anselmo knelt down and lifted the dog into his arms.

"*La última viaje, amigo*. No? You understand? You do, you do. I know you do."

Serbero squealed in his throat, a sound that dogs make of pain and delight and wanting.

"Yes, my friend." Anselmo held the dog close to his chest. He turned toward the sea. "The greatest journey."

From the window, Nicolas watched his great-grandpa carry the dog to the dock. The moonlight was so strong the sand sparkled. Anselmo made three more trips from the workshop to the dock. On his third trip, he dragged a rough-hewn pole and a long piece of stiff canvas. In a quarter-hour he had set sail and untied from the dock.

The canvas flapped listlessly and Anselmo sculled with the stern oar at first just to make some headway. But they met the breeze out past the end of the dock and bore off on a starboard tack past the little cay of the birds. Progress was slow but smooth and constant, so in short time Anselmo could look back and see his house and the workshop on the shore and the water tower beyond it. And the background of palms. Serbero twitched his ears and lifted his head at a sound. Angela and Nicolas stood on the dock waving good-bye.

Anselmo waved back silently. Serbero squealed but could not add anything else. He looked up balefully.

"The angels will know us," Anselmo told the dog. "Do not be worried."

Serbero lowered his head.

"Three kinds of things," he told the dog. "The Father, the Son, and the Holy Ghost. Three parts. But always loving, always loved. She is in the sand and in my arms, and in the spirit. Always loved. She gives us children and rum and waits for us to come. Holy spirits float over the sea in threes, the invincible angels will welcome us. On the greatest journey, *amigo*."

Angela and her son stood on the end of the dock and watched the sail go off into the sky, dissolving at last like a pearl. Three things. The flesh, the memory, the spirit. In a little boat named *Matilda*.

NIGEL ASSAM

Small Ode to the Hudson River

This river flows from the
force of someone's finger.

This river courses, like veins,
and begins from the shoulder,

and contains remnants of red.
This water begins in the pores

of springs, caresses stones in
the soil, and sands in the depths,

green cliffs full of houses and
faces flushed with shadows

leaning into the waves
yearning for water. White

waves stretch to the sides as
the river carries the train.

This river, full of dusty waves,
brown as the color of horses kicking

dirt, reflects the clouds as it passes
through Tarrytown under the bridge,

glistening with towns on its arms
and its Sunday-men still fishing.

With its arms, the river soothes the
stones beneath the towns,

and it brushes with a dapple
the rushing names of Hastings

and the wounded of Yonkers,
its hair reaching through the stones

on its sides. These waves, particles
of prayer-filled dust, become the

beacon of the Point and the star
of the state. These remnants still course

with the dust, the waves still rush
for the stones, the lines still lean

with the trees, with crowded shoulders,
and waves full of reflection stirring with pledge.

Last Night

The trams were running until three-thirty
in the morning over the East River
back and forth over Manhattan, and the upward
flow of barges in the tide in the night
The waves washed against the rocks behind the
wall where we sat, cartons and crates,
containers full of machinery going to homes
north of the river
and the sound of tires across the water beside
the wall
Last night was not Manhattan, nor was it
America
and the rats you imagined were never there
beneath the waves in the water
Over Roosevelt's stony face buried with bricks,
the cars carried back and forth millions of
restless and exhausted minds, ladies with short
hair, and fingernails, and skirts
The quiet avenue, and the future sight behind
the fence
and the river beneath the wall,
and the park with the solitary garbage standing
in the grass looking like a grave
Everywhere the leaves retired from the trees
beneath the night, the continual urge of
the barge against the tide
and the waves against the wall,

and the millions of invisible rats,
and the continual crossing of the river,
and we ended looking up under the half-smile
        of the reluctant moon

HEATHER PRINCE

Satellite

I watch a single star
Recline on the vapor
Of a passing jet
I dream
And wait for 3 am

Old moths brush kisses
Across my hair
Chasing
Blue tinges
That shadow the street light

The star moves
Over the alley
Leaving me
Alone with cats
And blossoming tomatoes

George Bernard Shaw ROBIN YANES

KELLY SCOTT

To Keep a Body Warm

"All right," Hank said, "let's get to work." He said it out loud, to no one in particular. The house was empty, quiet. He could hear the teakettle readying for the boil. Why was it always so cold here? *I swear,* he thought, *there aren't enough sweaters in this city to keep a body warm.*

He did the dishes while the tea bag steeped. He liked to use as little soap as possible. None at all would be best. The hot water would clean just fine. He didn't even use a sponge; just ran his fingers around the inside of each glass, feeling for any roughness—dried orange pulp, milk ring. The plates he scratched smooth with a fingernail.

He rubbed his reddened fingers across the clean plates until they made a squeaky sound. His hands felt puffy under the hot water, and he thought that if he squeezed his fingers together, they would spring back like a showroom mattress.

"Cold is something I cannot abide," he said. This he said out loud, too, because it seemed like a statement that shouldn't just rattle around in the head. "Abide" was a word no one used anymore, except maybe very formal ladies in the Deep South. But it seemed more serious than if you just said you couldn't stand something. "I simply cannot," he said again, as if the cold were an affront to his good name.

The old house was drafty, all right. But spring was

nearly here. No, that wasn't right, either. Winter passed yesterday. The new season brought snow flurries all the same. Hank wrapped the afghan more tightly around him. He imagined his sister, Joan, sitting right over there in that chair, working her crochet needle the way you'd navigate an airplane spoon of baby food. He'd bring her tea and she'd say to put it down on the TV tray and sit awhile.

When he was younger he couldn't sit still at all. Joan thought him foolish for it and told him so. "Where's the dang train?" she'd say. "I don't see any train leaving any Union Station. Now sit yourself down."

Sometimes on Saturdays the family would go to the beach. Hank was about twelve then. He'd slide down the walkway toward the sand in his drugstore thongs, balancing a canvas beach chair on his head. A blanket would be spread upon the sand and various heavy items laid at each corner. Hank would sit long enough to strip down to his swimsuit and then be off toward the shoreline, the volleyball courts, a patch of ice plant on the dunes. There he could look out over the vast stretch of beach and peer at groups of people on blankets, asking himself, "Is this my family?" He would study them from the hill, remembering his father's way of sitting or his mother's gesturing, eliminating a group for its radio or separate towels.

At last he would find them. There they were, two blankets down from the polka-dot beach umbrella that should have given them away immediately. His mother was lying on her stomach, reading, while his father began digging through the cooler.

Joan was reclined, as ever, on her back. She would stay this way all day if she could. Others would turn over or go to dip their feet in the sea. Joan slept. She had the completely relaxed body language of a stone drunk, moving only her toes to shovel a well down into cool sand.

Hank made his way back. He tried to imitate Joan. He lay down and closed his eyes. Blue stars began to form behind his eyelids. When he tried to chase them they darted away in the blackness. He turned his head until the background grew lighter, and he knew if he opened his eyes he would be blinded by the sun.

The heat made the chorus of radios sound funny. Hank thought it was the heat, anyway. He imagined the shimmering waves rising from the sand, carrying the sound away in a kind of audio hula dance. You could hear a song all the way down the beach, it seemed. Conversations from people several blankets over sounded as if they were being broadcast to Hank's ears, the way those little window speakers do at the drive-in.

After several minutes of eavesdropping he got up and announced he was going for a swim. His mother nodded, not looking up from her book.

"Sounds good," his father said. "Want some company?"

They walked toward the sea, his father in front. Hank forced his stride smooth through the hot sand. He imagined his feet turning to Mexican sandals, tire treads for soles, with each crease and whorl of footprint deep and tough as the bottom of a steel-belted radial.

The first wavelet lapped at their feet and made Hank wiggle his toes. He could feel sand crabs worming their way beneath the wet sand. That first tickling always made him stifle a giggle. With each new wave came a low muffled clattering, and when the sea washed back into itself Hank could see a bed of smooth rocks and shells where the first line of waves had broken.

He looked up at his father, who was scanning the beach for the two flags that marked the swimming-only section. He pointed them out. "Keep your bearings," his father said. "Don't want the surfers to get you."

With that, his father struck a linebacker pose and looked at Hank, grinning. He was not one of those who tested the water before a swim, or inched his way out beyond the shore breakers. "It's gonna be cold no matter what," he once said. "So you'd better get used to it quick."

Hank watched his father sprint through the flat water, then dive into a small wave. He followed when he saw his father surface. Hank first picked a path around two girls who had wandered with their mother to the water's edge. The girls were bent down, poking at a bulbous piece of kelp that had washed ashore. He began his run, swerving around them and picking up speed through the shallow water until he could feel it pushing at his legs.

He crashed through the first wave, then saw a bigger one behind it. Lowering his head, he dove in. The cold water was exhilarating. His feet found the bottom and he launched himself to the surface.

"Hey, Dad!" he shouted. Hank could see his father just beyond the breakers. He looked to be far, far out to sea. Hank was a good swimmer, but he was unsure of the current that might be at work. He ducked another wave, then turned toward the beach to be sure he was between the flags. The two girls had abandoned the kelp and were gingerly approaching the water, grabbing each other and screeching as they found themselves suddenly ankle-deep in each foamy surge.

He found he could walk a good deal of the way out. Once a wave had broken and had begun to recede, the water was only waist-high. He judged each wave as it came, timing a dive or vault to the moment before the wave crested. By now his father had seen him and was waiting.

When he reached his father he could no longer feel the sandy bottom, even during the trough before another gathering swell. They were beyond the waves now. The open sea lay ahead. Hank looked behind him. He had to squint to make out the girls, their mother, the flags, the lifeguard tower. It was always this way with his father.

"Can you touch bottom?" Hank asked. His father drew his arms above his head and plunged downward until only the tips of his fingers were showing above the water. "Yep," he said, when he had surfaced. They floated on their backs awhile then, letting the current carry them along. Hank felt his apprehension fade. He closed his eyes and let the water shift his trunk and arms in the small, jerky movements of an old man he had once seen in the grocery store, the one his mother said not to stare at.

In the last days of Joan's life she could hardly hold a cup, her hands shook so. Hank used to sit with her as she struggled to bring the straw to her mouth for a sip of ice water. It was here in this room that his sister Joan died. Simply died. It wasn't a remarkable thing. There was nothing more to do afterward but call the doctor and the rent-a-bed company and the funeral home. She passed, is all, Hank thought, like a meal that starts out savory and full of promise on a plate and ends up a little dollop of something fibrous in the bowl.

How could she know she would get some goddamn disease out here on this stupid cold plain that would put her in the ground down the street, at a cemetery full of Civil War babies? "What in hell were you doing out here, anyway?" Hank said. He blew on his tea and looked around the room. There wasn't much in it, really. An antique rocker in the corner with a red cushion for the back and another for the rump. A two-shelf bookcase with a reading lamp that had frills on the shade. A couch covered with a blue-and-white afghan. It looked like the living quarters of a person planning her next move.

She loved TV trays. Kept them in their cart beside the refrigerator. Before she had got bad enough to be bedridden she would set up two trays side by side at the couch and bring meals out to Hank. They would sit and stare out the big picture window while they ate baked potatoes or pea salad or steaks. She promised him fresh strawberries that they would pick from a patch in summertime out beyond the city limits.

"You've got TV trays. Why don't you have a TV to go with 'em?" Hank asked once.

"Got one right there," she said, looking out the big picture window.

Well, that was fine, but all you could get was the Weather Channel. He watched it now, a spit of snow that blew against the window but didn't stick. The trees were bare and slate colored, just like the yard. He was tired from being tensed all the time with cold. His muscles felt like they had gone cannibal, devouring each other to stay warm. He hated this place with his whole being, and the hatred had only raised the temperature around his skin a degree or two.

The house was his now. Joan had willed it to him, and told him so a few weeks before the end. "Stay here awhile," she had said. "See if you don't learn to like it."

He found himself going to her closet one afternoon to see what could be salvaged for charity. When he swung the door open the smell of her fabric softener wafted across him, and he stood there awash in a sadness he did not understand. He wasn't particularly close to Joan. She had asked him to come out from the coast to be with her because there was no one else who was family.

They were too different, was all. Always were. He supposed that even facing death they would be opposites. She lay there accepting everything that came at her, bathed in some congenital serenity or cowardice, which had always irritated him.

The closet was filled with clothes he'd never seen her wear. In the few months he'd been with her she mostly wore denim overalls with a red sweater wrapped around her. The overalls, three or four pair, were so equally faded you couldn't tell them apart. But the closet held dresses that looked almost new, nice enough for church. There were slacks, too, and long quilted coats with flowery designs.

He moved the clothes on their hangers to one side of the doweling until he came to a man's shirt printed with ears of corn on a cream-colored background. The ears were angled to the right or left so that they appeared to dance on the cotton material. They looked to be boy or girl ears, some with their silk gathered at the top in a ponytail or green husks pulled down and knotted at the waist with a length of rope.

Hank found that the shirt fit, kept it on, and finished with the rest of the closet. He bundled the clothes into a garbage bag and put it by the front door.

"Sweet corn, ain't it great, the thing in life that's worth the wait," he heard Joan say in a singsong lilt. Her voice came to him sometimes as through a telephone receiver where the connection was bad. Scratchy as a Victrola record, but there was no mistaking it was her. The things she said to him at these times were things he had heard her say in life, maybe months or years ago. All it took was a trigger to set her yakking away in his head.

Their mother had a patch of sweet corn growing in the backyard every summer when they were young. This was a rare thing in their suburban beachside neighborhood, to plant sweet corn when you could buy five for a dollar at the grocery store. To some it seemed a waste of good real estate. But the thing you couldn't buy was sweet corn in its infancy, when it was no bigger than a candy bar, its milky kernels the size of baby teeth. You couldn't buy the sight of tassels growing longer by the week and quivering in the salted wind.

Just before dinnertime, Hank's mother would send him and his sister out to the yard to pick the corn. It took ten minutes to inspect the stalks, looking for the ears that stood out as champions. There could be no pests burrowing beneath the green husks. Only the longest, most perfect shape would do. A few baby ears were eaten at the start of the harvest, when so many more were left to pick. Toward the end of the season, one had to lower the standards according to the supply, but now Hank could afford to be choosy.

He liked to walk the rows with his arms held out to his sides, like a living scarecrow. He let the long, shiny leaves brush against his bare skin. They tickled like the floppy ears of a basset hound. When they had finished, Hank followed Joan to the kitchen, where his mother had a pot of water boiling. She let them stand over a trash can to do the shucking; then she pulled off the last strands of silk Hank always missed, and put the corn into the water.

And then there was nothing to do but stand around, take deep breaths, and wait. Within minutes, the kitchen filled with a smell sweet and musty as the back of a baby's neck. The green husks in the wastebasket warmed, giving off the acrid scent of mown grass. The smells and the silk always reminded Hank of a bedtime story his mother read to him, and at the time he was sure it must be the smell of Rapunzel's hair.

Joan's eyes shone with a kind of rapture as she told Hank of the sweet corn that came from the Midwest. Honey and cream, it was called, and it tasted like no other corn in the world. You pulled back the husk to reveal a curved checkerboard in gold and white, each kernel so rich and sweet it was almost redundant to add melted butter. She said it was the memory of this corn, piled high in the back of pickup trucks at the farmers' market, that got you through a Midwest winter.

"California might be the Land of Milk and Honey," Joan said, "and maybe it's not anymore, and maybe it never was. But honey and cream is the real deal."

"Well, why can't you just grow it out there?" Hank said. "Seeds can cross state lines, you know. Take it to the San Joaquin, it'll be just the same. Maybe better."

She looked at him sadly, as you would an old dog whose hips had failed and could only lie around waiting for the food dish to be brought to it. She looked at him a long time, and with an expression of not understanding after years of trying to. Perhaps it was merely the profound fatigue of a long battle with disease.

"I don't know, Hank. I guess I don't want to know," she said. "This is where I found it."

WALLY SWIST

After Reading the Upanishads

When the wise knows that it is through the great and omnipresent Spirit in us that we are conscious in waking or in dreaming, then he goes beyond sorrow.

All day, I have sat
by the water. Now
it is time to walk
the streets of the island,
my footsteps echoing
over the cobbles,
the town's stone dwellings
streaked with the sky
at dusk. When I speak
with the master
at the hermitage,
he says I am welcome
to stay as long as I like.
Once, before waking,
I heard his voice
call my name, ringing

deep within me,
vibrating like a bell,
spreading out like ripples
clear across the water
in the bright morning.

Starflower

Star
of the upland woodlands,
seven-petaled,
not unlike the Pleiades'
seven sisters,
that speckles
the new green
of the undergrowth
beside the loose talus
of the trail
like flecks of sea foam
amid a bed
of browned pine needles,
springing out of
a whorl of leaves.
Wherever you bloom,
starflower,
your china white
blazes as if
it were fixed
like a pattern

of seven-pointed
starlight,
your petals set
like a constellation
against the shade
spread along
the mountain path
every May.
I see
you everywhere
since now
I know your name.

DANIELA HEGGEM

Sense of Sight

Turning the door handle
ever so cautiously
open the door
step in . . .

wicks glimmering like fireflies
shadows cast on the wall
of smooth lines, curves and bumps
silks shining reflection

from the dim light
a puff of smoke streams
from the shadow on the wall

"come in"

Taking the door handle
ever so cautiously
close the door
step in.

JERRY MONACO

Stolen Photos

I want to speak to you secretly of Deirdre. She was born in the middle of the century, a daughter of a doctor and a writer, who fancied themselves southern aristocrats. It was a small town and they were a respected, if slightly anachronistic, family. When I was visiting as a child I stole photographs of her, from a dresser drawer full of photographs, in the room they called the library. The theft was never discovered and when the house burned down a few months later all was lost except the photographs I confiscated. She was a strange beauty as a child, always stiff, full lips, and oval face. But it was the eyes that made the pictures of her different from the pictures of just another girl in a crinoline dress. Her eyes were huge and when caught unaware they looked glassy and stupid. Otherwise they looked simply malevolent; the kind of eyes you wouldn't dream of dreaming about but you do anyway.

Her childhood was arranged for her in the custom of agnostic southern families who have yet to consider that times have changed since the defeat of Reconstruction. There was church and school and ballet class and the black maid who did most of the caring. There were parties on the back lawn beneath the shade tree and around the stone fishpond, also catered by black servants. People and events moved regularly in this way until conscience interfered with the enjoyment of dead social forms. It is a well-known fact that in America, a nation which prefers to ignore history, a generally happy state of affairs is periodically disturbed by sudden historical kickbacks. In the southern territories it usually has something to do with the uncompleted revolution which they call the War Between the States and we Yankees refer to as the Civil War.

Deirdre left childhood with a wealth of memories and well it should be, since nostalgia is the one unalienable condition of exile. Her father was an unhappy liberal and in the heat of the times his house was burned down by segregationists, his practice went to hell, his wife left him and the children and moved to San Francisco with a famous Beat poet, and he began to consume an amount of alcohol appropriate to the situation of a fallen southern gentleman. Events followed their usual course and he died. It's no use dismissing all of this as just the usual cocktail party chattering summation of a life, because, even though it is just that, it is nevertheless what actually happened. It is not the writer's fault if finer sensibilities find reality objectionable simply because it happens over and over again in the same way.

So there she was in 1966, a vague young woman of seventeen, with an appropriate scorn for what she thought of as the middle class, and with many inappropriate notions concerning the uselessness of morality, all in fitting with her time and place. No one blamed her for her anger and all agreed that circumstances had cheated her of a normally happy life. But this did not prevent her from being a useful object lesson to the community. Perhaps it was her function as a living morality tale that brought her to doubt morality's utility. This is mere speculation on my part and I think it is probably better to stick to the surface of events. I only bring it up because I wish the reader to refrain from treating her in the same way as the townspeople did. She was a beautiful young woman and in spite of the fact that mothers pointed her out to their children as someone who should be felt sorry for, the young men of the town—oh, but compared to her they were mere boys—included her in their fantasies and even considered the possibility of a long future of married nights by the side of her naked body, her long muscular legs, her soft high breasts and those eyes. . . . Well, those eyes were a bit of a problem in the fantasies of the young men, they couldn't be avoided, and they always seemed to know too much about the boy they looked at, or possibly, through. Quite frankly, they made people uncomfortable and prevented many members of the opposite sex from attempting to fulfill their dark fantasies. In a less enlightened age than our own she would have been accused of being a witch, burned at the stake, and planted at the crossroads. In view of this she left town for New York City, ostensibly because she was given a full scholarship to NYU, which at that time was trying to diversify its student body with people from foreign lands and Mississippi was graciously included in this category because (unlike Florida, a New York colony) few New Yorkers ever visited that distant state.

In New York she sat in her room or in clubs and cafés smoking cigarette after cigarette and exhaling smoke into the faces of her companions. She always wore black and this contrasted favorably with her cropped hair and cream skin. She never lost her southern accent but overcame it enough to talk as fast as any New York Jew or Italian. She stared at her boyfriends blankly when they talked of sex (nobody talked of love back then) or politics, usually in the same breath. She took them to bed and threw them out before morning. She never talked of the past and nobody knew she had one that was worth talking about. The men didn't even seem to care one way or another. This was still an age when men didn't think about listening to women. She made all the men she knew mad because none of them could figure out what she wanted. It was a constant refrain she heard as she broke up with one man after another. "What do you want anyway?" they would say. And she would look at them with unnerving eyes and say, "Not you, honey." Or, what was even more infuriating, she would just giggle as if the question were absurd. She was doing a good imitation of a bohemian about then, but what I think she really wanted was to upset the world. I don't think she ever realized that the world was upsetting enough without her help.

It was somewhere in this period that I saw her once again, in a basement of an old warehouse, reciting poetry in front of an audience. She didn't see me. I was in the back of the dark room and she was surrounded by lights. I didn't recognize her at first. She seemed older than her years and anger tends to distort the features. Between stanzas she would inhale her cigarette, turn her head to the side, and let the smoke go to the ceiling in one long stream. I think this was part of her act. People were shouting and laughing, and finally she left the stage and everybody clapped. After that I saw her often around the Village, in cafés, in lofts converted into theaters, declaiming, reciting, performing, and doing something we all called art at that time. She never saw me and I always acted my role of spy.

For six years, until 1973, she lived across from the old Jefferson Market courthouse. There was a women's prison there at the time, and I could never stand on the street opposite her window for long without being harangued by prisoners commenting on my sexual proclivities. Protests and wars raged throughout the world and in 1969 my friends thought revolution was around the corner, but I calmly dallied across the street from a woman who didn't even remember me, and braved the insults of female convicts. I knew the crowd she ran in. They all talked in quotation marks and made faces at those who didn't. They believed they were making art and I believe some actually were. They stood on blocks of ice and sang songs, they did political clown shows in the street, they smoked grass and went to art shows. They were not the kind to join the SDS, though they all thought deeply and profoundly about politics. They were elitists. Their elitism consisted of one belief: everything made by humankind was neither true nor false but merely artifice. They thought they were avant-garde and to prove this wrong the ones who succeeded ended up as the mainstays of the art world. The others found themselves on Wall Street, where twenty years later their belief in artifice was proved correct. But such mysteries remain outside the heart and I won't deal with them here.

Deirdre's promise was never fulfilled. Surely she was as good as the rest of them. In a dance choreographed to spliced-together sections of Rolling Stones' songs she formed the audience into a circle and danced in and out of the shadowy arms of our body spaces. She worked the audience as if she were a shaman and, I think, we were entranced. She was not ungraceful and her poetry, though lacking in rhythm, was full of images and disconcerting juxtapositions of nouns, a style that was very popular. But her true art seemed to be dangling moments. She would get a chance to choreograph a dance, but the next day she would insult the director of the dance company by seducing his lover. Her poetry would be accepted by a well-known literary magazine and then she would go out of her way to sleep with the editor and then kick him out the door, half naked, at 3 A.M., as was her usual wont. Her only explanation was that she liked to sleep alone. It was easy to keep track of her escapades from a distance. The whole crowd talked about them, laughed about them, sneered at them, yelled about them across crowded rooms.

With her attitude no one ever expected her to consent to marriage or even to living with a man. But presently her life twisted in strange ways. Her apartment was broken into and ransacked. There were rumors about a secret life that none of us could comprehend. In San Francisco her mother died in a car accident along with her lover the Beat poet and there was some suggestion in the police report that it might not have been an accident at all. Her brother, who had come to New York and had actually lived with her for a couple of weeks, was found in an apartment on the Lower East Side dead of an overdose of heroin. Finally there was a fire in her building, which started in her apartment, and she was forced to move. The scene had finished and nobody seemed to know how or why. It was just a short one-act play but all expected it to go on and on. For six years no one looked beyond the next month, the next day, the next cup of coffee, and then it was over, all so soon. The end of the act seemed to coincide with Deirdre's departure from the Village.

She lost touch with the crowd. We heard she had married some man who owned a fleet of cement trucks and another fleet of garbage trucks. The crowd all laughed and winked knowingly. The cement man's residence was in New Jersey (the gang laughed some more at this), but she spent most of the year in their winter home on Key Biscayne. She took Spanish lessons at the University of Miami and spent long hours walking on the beach and then sitting alone reading Kafka or Celine or Dostoevsky in neatly refrigerated rooms. Nights she spent prowling the bars and when she woke up in the morning, in the cold room humming with artificial air, her hands and limbs shook until she remembered where she was, who she was with, and what she had done the night before. She was not a vegetarian, but she ate nothing but a few vegetables for dinner and peanuts and potato chips with her drinks. She was never plump and now she lost weight. Her husband came down twice a month on weekends and for the whole month of December. He had his own business to attend to, so the two didn't bother each other. In this way her body trundled down to thirty without notice of the passing years, though each individual minute cut with rusty gears.

Then one day at an art exhibit, in the rooms and hallways of the mansion down the block, the home of a cocaine importer, she met her friend Peter, an artist from the old days in the Village. He was broke but his paintings were just catching on, he said. They talked for an hour about the past and what had happened to all their friends and she took him home. . . . And later in bed that night, "Why don't you come back to New York," he said. And she laughed, raspingly, deep in the throat, and without humor and told him how that was impossible. "But you should know that," she said and then let slip, "I thought everyone knew about . . ." and stopped. Her life wasn't an open book and no one really knew what had happened to her. If you will permit the writer a guess (there is no way for me to be certain and permission must always be granted on these matters) I would say that the realization she was alone with her knowledge shocked her. . . . "Why don't you stay in Miami," she said to him.

The last time I talked to Pete was in 1982 when he called to tell me to send his things to Coral Gables because he had found a place and had decided to stay in the Miami area. Three years later I saw his photograph on the inside pages of the *Daily News*. The headline was "Crime Boss Murdered by Wife's Lover." He was found guilty and sentenced to life in prison. Deirdre was never found. Perhaps she's in Argentina.

The circumstances of the evidence can always point an arrow to the guilty, but the arrow was through my heart, and because of this I can only insist that she lived a life of innocence.

LINDA BRUNNER

Para Frieda y Diego

On Valentine's Day
I take two posters
from a portfolio
and hang them on the wall.
One is a photo
in black and white
of a small, beautiful woman
in traditional dress
eyes dark and direct.
The other a painting
of an Indio woman
arms encircling
a dazzling bouquet of lilies
the colors subdued
yet rich
her hair in two joined plaits.
I live in the shadow
of those two great artists.
I honor their humanity
their creativity
and their ability
to suck noisily
on the straw of life.

LAKE BOGGAN

What I Wanted to Say

If you ask me where I come from
I will say my father who was a cowboy.
Page after page will tell you, he moved the Western wind,
flattening his horse against the strength of mountains.
Deep snow and prairies became the man;
his long bones angular and handsome.
When he touched the heels of his boots
into the red clay of Colorado, he shaped me.

His brain was a forum where all thought was possible.
I leaned into him when he spoke.
He spoke like the wind
that spreads seeds and moves water.
He knew the language of all creatures.
As time passed he asked the sky
to teach the harsh language of aging.
He asked the opinion of beasts and stones.

I ask if you remember how large he stood,
pointing to the stars for me.
"Orion, count the diamonds in his belt
and there his hands and feet.
When I die," he said, "I will go to Orion,

together we will protect you."
He stood like that, feet apart
or sat in his blacksmith shop
at his red enameled piano
beating out honky-tonk.
His religion was the immensity of the universe.
He danced a jig with me.

Midway into my life, Apollo, Lord of the Silver Bow,
struck my father with Parkinson's
that feasted on the man the gods had loved.
He was sacrificed slowly and bit by bit
until I could not watch,
until I was dying with him.
He burned out like the fire of Hephaistos
who had shod the feet of my father's horses.

When the Baptist who was my sister
dragged him long into the prayers of simpletons
through the dust of strangers and Christians,
I did not recognize the jello salad sermon
the milk-blue reverend who stood
on my father's coffin to call the faithful.
The flocks who stole my father's carcass
did not tell the hymn of his life.
They used the excuse of his great dying
to increase their numbers.
I turned away, towards the sun that rid me of the sight
and the song of crickets that deafened me.

When my father's dry bones were alone,
I returned by a path no one knew.

I carved his stone as it should have been,
my wailing into the prairie moon,
I danced, played his red piano and drank his whiskey.
I told his words over his grave and called to Orion:
"Take this horseman into the starry night."

MATTHEW KANE MARKHAM

Givre

The beauty of Paris is celebrated throughout the Christian world. Its grand cathedrals, the vibrant Seine, the majesty of the Louvre—they are eternal fountains of inspiration, cascading passion and joy into the human spirit. But in the heart of the City of Light there is a darkness, an abyssal place from which few emerge with both their lives and their sanity. During the reign of the thirteenth Louis, when I was in the autumn of my twenty-fifth year, the Bastille became my home.

I had published a pamphlet, and though my views were essentially royalist, I had discussed too honestly the questionable role of the church in our government. Richelieu, that damnable cardinal, deemed my views dangerous to the state, and I was cast into the dismal underworld of the Bastille where my words could not reach the ears of men. At first proud and indignant, by the fourth month I had fallen into utter despair, my humanity beaten, another nameless, hopeless wretch surrounded by masonry, miasma, and darkness.

Many died that winter. Each day carts carried away the bodies of the dead. How I envied them their freedom! Yet despite their deaths, the Bastille was bursting with enemies of the state and the church. Soon, by necessity, men were forced to share even the tiniest cells, such as my own. Thus it was that in the cold of February, when I believed my horror could grow no further, the man known as Givre *le Terreur* was cast in with me.

He was cruel of face, with dark eyes that hated and a thin mouth that sneered perpetually his disdain for mankind. His hair and beard grew ragged and unkempt—in truth, so did my own—lending a feral quality to his countenance. I knew him at once.

All of France had heard of Givre. He had killed some dozen men the previous year, cutting throats for a purse, a meal, or—in one case—a bottle of Burgundy. Nor were women and children safe from his violence. The stories were as gruesome as they were numerous. He had cast Paris in a terror that was relieved only briefly when he was captured the previous April. He had escaped then on the eve of his execution and had not been heard of again by the time of my own arrest. Now, seeing him for the first time in person, his fearsome aspect only confirmed that he was utterly inhuman, incapable of remorse, compassion, or any other emotion that defined the goodness in humankind.

Horror seized me at once, and I begged the *geôliers* not to leave me alone with him. My desperate entreaties caused their amusement and nothing more. The door fell to, and the sound of the dropping bolt echoed a death knell in my head.

I stood apart from Givre as he sat against the mildewed wall. The light was dim, but I could see that he smiled at me with rotten teeth, a smile of amusement rather than amity. "I won't kill you," he said, but the soulless, murderous timbre of his voice was too unsettling for me to believe him.

"I'm not defenseless," I lied, affecting a strength I might once have possessed.

A sincere chortle arose from his throat. "You don't believe me," he said. "You will."

"They'll hang you tomorrow, will they not?" I could not suppress the hopefulness in my voice.

"Tomorrow is the Sabbath. They'll wait until *lundi.*"

"Small difference," I reminded him.

Givre made no reply, but simply smiled, curled up on the stone floor, and went promptly to sleep.

I shook my head in disbelief. Givre *le Terreur* in my cell! In turn I silently cursed my luck, my king, Richelieu, and the Bastille. I had by then grown expert at their malediction.

I spent that day watching Givre in the meager light of the cell, thinking all the while of my wife. I wondered if she might hear of my death at the hands of the infamous *Terreur,* a last murder to consecrate his soul's journey to hell.

When night fell the darkness was impenetrable. Still, I remained alert, listening for any movement, expecting at any moment to feel Givre's brown hands around my throat. When morning came at last, the light revealed him still to be sleeping, unmoved, curled in peaceful slumber.

Givre arose soon after the dawn and wordlessly moved to the door. He pushed his ear against it and shut his eyes.

"What are you doing?" I asked, unable to control my tongue after so many months of solitude.

"I'm listening for the *voiture de la mort*. Did you rest?"

"I did not."

"You should have. We will need our strength."

"How is it that you can sleep so well, with a heart heavy with murder?"

"My heart is not heavy, *monsieur*. Men who worry over heaven and hell are troubled by their crimes. I have no doubts. My infernal eternity is assured."

His words gave me pause, and he returned his attention to the door. A minute passed, and I asked why he waited for the death cart. Only the Bastille could make a man so indiscriminately conversant.

"When it comes, we will escape," he replied. "You wish to escape, do you not?"

"Oui, bien sûr!" I said, growing keen. "But how?"

Givre came to life suddenly, and I thought for a moment he would attack me. Instead he lay across from the door and said, "Begin shouting that I've killed myself. Be loud, and do not stop until the guards come." He leaned against the wall then, his head cocked unnaturally to one side. I understood his game at once, and in my deep desire for freedom I embraced it, raising a din that promptly brought the guards' attention. They entered cautiously, but their suspicions were put to rest when one *geôlier* kicked Givre. He fell over, eyes open and vacant, his tongue lolling unnaturally upon the filth-ridden stone flags. I myself believed for a moment that he might actually be dead.

The *voiture de la mort* was brought, a deep barrow already loaded with three unfortunates, their spotty limbs reaching lifeless from its rails. Givre arose then from death, taking the guards and cart master by surprise. He killed them brutally, crushing their skulls against the walls I hated so bitterly.

When the deed was done, Givre laughed in self-satisfaction as I retched, sickened by the sight of such savagery. I realized then how futile my night's vigil had been. I had neither the ability nor the will to fight a savage like Givre. Concession and flight would be my only viable policies with him.

We escaped then, I in the clothes of the cart master and Givre hidden in the pile of bodies. I marveled at his resolution, lying motionless among the diseased, jaundiced, bloodied corpses. A man in his element, I recall thinking.

Our subterfuge saw us out of the Bastille, and I beamed prodigiously at the grand sun. By no means could I have concealed my exultation, and I am certain I seemed quite mad to the Parisians I passed. The joyful *porteur de le cadavre* on his way to the pyres at Crue-strasse!

On a quiet street, I wheeled the cart to an alley beside a stable. I hoped to part with Givre then, but he arose from the pile and followed me. I urged him to wait and disguise himself, but he said doing so would entail waylaying someone, a dangerous undertaking so soon after escape. The livery master would have been an obvious choice, I thought, but the lucky man was neglecting his duty and was nowhere to be found. I stole a horse, and at Givre's insistence I carried him behind me. He had no command of horses, and he wished to leave the city as swiftly as I.

Taking great care to avoid the constabulary we fled Paris, and nightfall found us on the road to Amiens, where I wished to collect my wife before fleeing to England.

I cannot express my revulsion at having Givre so near to me. His hands, which had broken necks and shattered skulls, defiled women and strangled children, held firmly to the coat I had taken from the cart master.

The cold was severe, but Givre still wore rags, and his

feet were quite bare. Again I tried to impress upon him the suspiciousness of his appearance and thus encourage him to wander off to rob a cottage and clothe himself. He agreed with me, but he said it was not yet time, wishing to wait until that evening despite the bitter cold.

We hurried our overburdened horse, stopping occasionally to give it rest. In the evening we stole some immature turnips from a country garden. They were bitter but nourishing, and our shrunken stomachs soon were filled.

The cold grew more intense. It cut mercilessly through our inadequate clothing, and we were forced to make an early camp. We found a likely spot well off the main road, where I, a skilled woodsman, managed a fire by friction. Soon we were comfortably warm.

There were lights in a village some miles away, and I hinted that Givre could find food and clothing there. I still feel shame, these many years later, at how easily I invited suffering upon innocent souls merely to diminish my own. My only excuse is my humanity—weak, flawed, and ignoble.

Givre ignored my suggestion, wishing to remain with me. He was certainly no fool, seeing plainly that I was his greatest chance of escape. I could manage the palfrey, and I could most certainly be relied upon not to give him over to the authorities, which would renew my own sentence. I was assured, at least for a time, of my safety from Givre.

My sleep was not the furtive, anxious nodding one might expect of a fugitive. I slept soundly, as a prince might. Only those who have seen the inside of the Bastille can understand the lightness of my soul, even in such grim circumstances. If but for that one night, I was free.

When dawn came Givre awakened me. He was clothed now better than I. He wore a coat of wool and shoes that, despite being much too large, would keep his feet warm as we rode. With a pleased grin he explained that he had visited the village in the night, and he warned me that parties of the king's soldiers were out in force, patrolling the highways in search of us.

We set off again into a white, somber day. The morning brought snow, and the cold deepened with my anxiety. Fearful of soldiers, we clung to the woods, moving ever closer to my home in Amiens. I was miserable with cold, as was the disheartened palfrey, but Givre was warm enough in his purloined garments.

Givre asked me of my plans, and I replied honestly that I wished only to join my wife and leave the country. By the manner of his query I understood his intention to keep me near at hand until he was confident of evasion—even if it meant following me to England. Though I loathed the thought of his extended company, I knew this protected me from his violence. I resolved to be patient and abandon him as soon as possible.

At dusk we stopped to rest and water our horse. My country home was scant miles away, and we would reach it that evening. I knew well that country, and I had guided us to a lake where the palfrey could drink. It was frozen over and covered with the falling snow, but we split the ice with some rocks and waited for her to drink her fill.

Givre and I wandered over the snowy ground to keep our blood flowing. I was impatient for home, and I wondered, not for the first time, how I might find my wife. Would she be there? Would she be well? Had she—I knew it was possible—found comfort with another man?

My thoughts were disturbed when I found a purse in Givre's tracks. I picked it up, and by its weight judged its contents to be gold. "You have dropped something, Givre," I called to him, holding it up for him to see.

Turning, *le Terreur*'s eyes became furious, and his voice raged unintelligible syllables as he started toward me. I feared as he leapt toward me that his avaricious wrath would overcome his sense and he would strike me down. But he had crossed onto the ice, and as he bounded toward me he fell through with a crash and disappeared! There was only silence then, and I knew he was trapped beneath the ice.

My first instinct was elation. I moved to the palfrey and had one foot in the stirrup when I was stopped by a strange, sympathetic impulse rising from deep within my soul. The dark, jagged hole in the perfect white of the frozen lake could not but remind me of the Bastille.

I had heard stories of men trapped beneath ice, and I have reflected many times since on what Givre *le Terreur* felt at that moment. Disoriented, panicked, surrounded by darkness and impossible cold. One reaches for freedom and finds instead an impenetrable, frozen wall. Lethargy and panic battle for control of one's limbs, and then come helplessness and the certainty of death. This was no doubt Givre's state when my hand found his and I jerked him from the watery oubliette and into the world of the living. Given the chance to rid myself and the world of Givre *le Terreur,* I found that I had not the heart to abandon even a wretch such as he.

Givre gasped and roared his lungs' relief. He had no strength, and I dragged him, helpless, to the shore. Knowing that delay would cause his death, I worked quickly to build a fire.

Givre had lost both his coat and his shoes in the lake, and he was fairly blue when the fire at last gained strength.

For two hours he sat silent and shivering, watching me tend the blaze. I had returned to him his purse, procured I knew not where, to prevent further impetuous acts of violence.

In time Givre's clothes dried and his color was restored. Yet still he fixed me with his dark eyes. At last, many hours into the night, he stammered the question, "Wh-why?"

I asked what he meant.

"Why did you pull me from the lake? I was dying."

"*Oui.* I know you were," I replied. "I could not stand by and celebrate while another man died. Not even you, Givre."

"You did in the Bastille."

"That was self-preservation."

"And this?"

I had no answer. Perhaps the difference was that in the Bastille, Givre had done the killing. On the lake all responsibility, and ultimately judgment, would fall squarely upon myself.

"Do you not wish to escape from me?" he asked.

"I do."

"Do you not fear me?"

"I do."

"Do you know some of the things I've done?"

"I've heard stories."

"They are true, *monsieur.*" His relentless eyes still held me, and I watched the fire rather than meet them. "You thought I had more money," he said after a minute's thought, but he meant it as a question.

"Very well," I replied and wondered at his lack of gratitude. He seemed incapable of understanding an act of kindness, as if none had been shown to him the whole of his life.

"Why then?" he asked. His brow was furrowed, as one trying to grasp a principle beyond one's limits, such as algebra or solar astronomy.

"Because, Givre, I've no wish to spend the rest of my life haunted by the memory of allowing a man to die. I'm going to sleep. We'll reach my home in the morning."

Givre released a mirthless laugh at my reply, but he pressed me no further. Yet still I felt his gaze upon me until the welcome maiden Sleep wrapped me in her compassionate embrace.

My anticipation the next morning was frightful, and we reached my small estate at a gallop. As I crossed the threshold of my modest château my body was quivering, from anxiety rather than from cold. No servants attended the door, and I surmised, correctly, that hardship had forced Margot to release them from service. I hurried from room to room, intent upon finding her.

I bounded up the stairs and found at last, alone in our bed, my Margot fast asleep. I was overjoyed at the sight of her, doubly so for the evidence of her faithfulness. I made a conscious effort to compose myself, knowing she would be overwhelmed if I unleashed all at once the tremendous exultation of my heart.

She was beautiful, then as now, my Margot. I knelt at her side and took her warm little hands in my own. She was frightened when she awakened. She did not recognize me, but when I spoke her name she cried her joy and embraced me as I had dreamed of for so many months.

It was some time before our mutual tears and caresses slowed. Drawing back then to look at me with piteous eyes, Margot started in fright. I had forgotten Givre. He stood in the doorway watching us—as I imagine he had the entirety of our reunion—with speculative, wondering eyes that betrayed his lack of understanding for our joy.

I said a few words in excuse of our haggard appearance and introduced Givre as Raul Duchesne. I explained quickly what had happened to bring us there and the necessity to leave within the hour. Indeed, for all I could guess the king's soldiers were without presently.

I washed, shaved, and dressed, and I felt reborn. Once again I was Gerard Haute, my gentleman's dignity restored. My wife implored Givre to take boots and a coat, but to my great surprise he sullenly refused, wrapping his bare feet in swaths torn from his own vest.

We provisioned ourselves for a two days' journey—long enough to reach Abbeville—and collected what little money we had. There was no way to conceal it from Givre, but we could not do without it.

I took also a pistol, primed and loaded, and put it in the pocket of my coat. I had no wish to use it, but if it made the difference of our freedom—from the king or from Givre—I most certainly would.

At last we saddled two fresh horses, the remains of my once-proud stable. We rode throughout the day, Margot upon her palfrey and Givre and I upon a strong bay. We rested seldom and were watchful of soldiers upon the road. Margot told me as we traveled of all that had happened since my arrest. I learned then of our ruined finances, though I considered it an act of mercy that Louis had not confiscated our home.

Arising from camp on the second day, I daresay we felt we had slipped from Richelieu's grasp. We continued at a steady pace, conserving our horses' strength now that Paris was well a hundred miles behind us.

I asked Givre his intentions, and as I had suspected, he stated his desire to flee with us across the channel. I disliked the thought of his continued presence, and I know Margot sensed my fear for her well-being. I wondered if she had guessed his true name. Still, so long as Givre was not violent

I could bear it. And I was no longer defenseless, having now a pistol to give me courage.

At mid-afternoon we spotted the soldiers, and moments later they us. They were some half-mile distant, riding in a group behind us on the snow-covered road. We had stopped to rest and eat, but now we remounted and trotted away, hoping not to arouse the soldiers' suspicions. We were disappointed, for they broke into a gallop as soon as we had begun.

We kicked our horses sharply then, hoping their mounts were not as well rested. For minutes we raced, but we found ourselves losing ground quickly to the king's grain-fed stallions.

Rounding a bend in the road, we reined in sharply. The river Somme lay before us. It was not frozen, but it was in flood—deep, treacherous, and unfordable. It was passable at such times only by means of a ferry, which at that moment was drawn up on the opposite bank some hundred yards distant.

The soldiers were closing, so close behind us now that we could hear their shouting. In a panic I led us at a gallop down a track that paralleled the river's course. At times it ran along the riverbank; at others it veered away through the dense brambles that grew over the bank until sight of the river was lost entirely.

We charged down this path at a dangerous pace, and yet after a few minutes we still could hear the pursuit behind us. Our horses foamed as we lashed them in our desperation, and bloody whorls of vapor arose from their nostrils to evince their misery. The sounds of pursuit grew still louder over the thickets, and we raced on.

Margot, her horse less burdened, had traveled ahead a few dozen yards, and she reined in suddenly before us.

Alerted, I did the same and immediately understood why. Through a break in the brush ahead I saw the red surcoats of the cardinal's legionaries. We were surrounded!

And so we stood on the snow-covered track, with capture behind and before us, and treacherous thickets to either side. I dismounted quickly, driven by a fear of the Bastille that Margot could not understand. "This way," I said, gesturing to the brambles. "They will not follow."

"It isn't possible," Margot said, dismounting nonetheless. Had she known what I knew, what Givre knew, she would have rushed headlong through the briers without further encouragement. As it was, I showed my courage by beginning, swatting aside some vines to form a path, though their thorns stung bitterly. A man shouted nearby, giving Margot and Givre the impetus to follow.

I led us toward the river. My hope was that we might find a log or some such thing to carry us away with the current and thus defy pursuit.

My jacket and gloves were of thick hide, as were Margot's, but we had to pick the briers from our faces and trousers. We moved as quickly as possible, and though it cost us many a scratch, we soon had a screen of vines between us and the soldiers. They were close now—close enough that we could hear the captain's exclamation when he saw the path we had chosen. It occurred to me then that the soldiers might loose a volley into the thicket, and I made Margot go before me that I might shield her with my body.

My concern for Margot had made me forget Givre. I turned to see if he followed, and I could not help but exclaim, foolishly, *"Mon Dieu!"* at the sight of him. Indeed he was behind us, picking his way through the treacherous briers without coat, gloves, or shoes. Yet he struggled on, his face anguished at the constant pulling, piercing, tearing of his flesh. He was covered in blood, rent with thorns from toe to crown. His feet, cut mercilessly through the swathings upon them, left red tracks in the snow. His hands were cut still worse. Torn from his wrists to his palms, Givre spilled blood upon the vines as he pulled them from his path. Well I knew that I would endure the same misery to escape the bleak depths that threatened us.

My foolish shout drew a hail of iron. Balls tore through the brush as the cracks of many rifles concussed our eardrums. Gratefully, their volley was ineffective, and we continued in cautious quiet.

We came at last to the bank, where, like a boon from above, an oared boat had drifted into the shoal. Its planks were rotting, but we cared little the mode of our salvation.

Reaching the opposite shore, we made haste for Abbeville. We walked without stopping throughout the night, giving no thought to food or rest, wishing only to leave France forever. Weary, aching, and cold we continued, yet neither I nor Margot spoke a word of complaint. The misery of Givre was far worse than our own, but he bore himself silently, refusing aid though anguish racked his face.

We crossed the city in the small hours before dawn and hurried to the docks, where a steady stream of ships departed for England and other lands. I am thankful we did not have to walk through the crowded streets. Givre would certainly have been detained for his extraordinary appearance.

In the growing light of the pre-dawn we reached the docks, finding them alive with activity. Only among the coarse and worldly seafarers could Givre pass without notice.

Making queries among the sailors, we learned that a

Dutch trader at the end of the pier would be sailing at dawn for London. The ship's purser could well see our desperation, and I spent nearly all the money we had securing passage for myself and Margot. Givre made separate but similar arrangements, and we boarded the *Schonblut* to await the captain's order to sail.

Our anticipation for the moment of our freedom grew with the light of dawn, and I felt my breast might burst from the pounding anxiety therein. At last we heard someone say that we would sail in ten minutes.

It was then that we saw the soldiers. They were passing from ship to ship, having words with the officers of each. Had we sailed immediately we might have evaded them, but it was clear they would reach us long before we cast off our moorings. We had run to the edge of France, and now there was nowhere further to go.

I placed my arm reassuringly around Margot and offered what comfort I could. "Have faith, Margot. All will be well," I said. "Do not worry, *mon rayon.* They may free you."

"*Et vous,* Gerard?" She began to weep.

What of me? Already I felt the walls of the Bastille around me, and I thought then of Givre. I looked about, but he was not on deck. Perhaps I could escape again, as he did. It was not beyond imagining, and yet. . . . It was too much to hope for. I determined then to take my own life, to free myself forever from the reach of cardinals and kings. As the soldiers approached the *Schonblut*'s gangplank I kissed Margot and reached for my pistol.

A musket shot rang over the dock, stopping my hand and scattering the king's soldiers as a ball splintered the planks beneath their feet. Behind the soldiers, on the deck of a Portuguese corvette, stood Givre *le Terreur,* my pistol smoking in his hand. The soldiers charged away from us as I watched the crew of the corvette fall upon Givre and lash him by his wrists to a spar.

To this day I can shut my eyes and see Givre, emaciated, cut and bloodied and clothed in rags, his arms stretched painfully to either side. I see the king's officer raise his rifle and I hear the report as Givre's head bends in death.

At just that moment the sun arose over Abbeville, casting Givre in silhouette. The brightness quickly grew to be more than my eyes could bear, and I was forced to look away. I had not realized it, but the *Schonblut* had by then cast off her moorings, and we were well under way.

I wondered for a few minutes over Givre's bold, defiant, final act. He had eluded capture. He had only to remain hidden until the soldiers had gone to make whole his escape. Had he stolen my pistol to indulge himself in a last act of murder? I wished to believe that he had died for myself and Margot, out of charity and kindness and sacrifice, but such concepts were foreign to him, and I could not believe this.

And yet, when the cold salt air sent my hands into the warmth of my deep coat pockets, I found with wonder the purse of gold he had once guarded with such animal cupidity.

Givre, I have no doubt, was judged harshly for his crimes. My prayers each night are for his soul. His name arises still when men speak of infamy and of criminals who distinguished themselves by their ruthlessness. But I wonder sometimes, of all the men who have cursed him in this life, how many died even half so nobly? Who among them ever embraced the virtue of self-sacrifice to such a degree?

Some would say these words are lies, or that my conclusions are madness. So be it. They cannot erase the debt I owe to him that died for me. Their scorn may fall upon my head like the raining spears of heaven, but always will I aver that Emil Henri Givre, the Terror of Paris, was my friend.

MICHELE STUART

Haiku

Seventeen syllables often linking
two thoughts
seemingly unrelated—
an underlying pattern
sensed, but never stated—

The sparrow hunts worms
In the garden—Monsoon rains
Flood the rice paddies.

Not
One thought following,
logically,
from another—

Slamming door echoes
Behind you—My heart cracks like
The porcelain bowl—

but,

Monsoon rains flood the
Rice paddies—My heart cracks like
The porcelain bowl.

The traditional rhythm
is five seven five—Usually,
a season is implied,
to set the mood—

Slamming door echoes
Behind you—In the garden
Sparrows hunt for worms.

But form serves image above all—
A picture, a feeling
captured—

Slamming door shatters
The porcelain bowl—my heart
Outside, sparrows sing.

DEBRA WILLIAMS

Anticipation

anticipating . . .
I have waited all my life
love, to be with you

PETER McNAMARA

Wind Chill Factor

Day breaks cold, whistles: Freeze.
Chain-link fences wind around factories
closed for the last time.
I am on a train out of Chicago, heading home.
We slide past the rumps of Pennsylvania towns, mean,
getting meaner,
willing to take cold and crack it
just to hear
something else snap.

River

Across a cold river
lamps flicker.
I rock on my porch
until the lamps darken.
Then row over, dock.

November morning:
this river shakes a convenient fog.
I stay warm
by torching your plans
for a simple bridge.
The river serves as my road
and my edge.

JUDITH MARTIN STRAW

Buying Thyme

Brian parked the car carefully, the strangeness of parking on the wrong side of the street breaking up habits like which shoulder to look over, which way to turn the wheels. Mentally, it was the wrong side of the street, but this was a one-way, and cars facing the same direction were parked on both sides. Satisfied that he hadn't left too much space between the car and the curb, he killed the engine and adjusted the rearview mirror to check his face. He decided that he was just looking slender, and not gaunt. Maybe he was really putting some weight back on. He smiled to his reflection, which smiled back. "You are kidding yourself." He picked up the empty canvas bag from the passenger's seat, checking quickly for traffic, got out, and headed to the farmers' market.

It was still early. He liked to get there early and see all the stuff on display: the white plastic buckets filled with flowers, the piles of oranges and lemons, the bins of avocados and tomatoes, the long tables covered with heads of lettuce and ears of corn. The early hours of the farmers' market gave him a visual cornucopia he could summon up in his mind at any time later in the week when he felt hopeless and bereft.

Which was happening more and more often these days.

He walked down the rows of stalls, smiling and nodding to the people hawking their produce, remembering Andrew's funeral last Tuesday. In the dim yellowish light of the funeral parlor, his eyes had glazed over with tears, but when he shut them to stop himself from weeping, his mind had presented him with the image of the farmers' market. All the sweet, fresh food, so perfectly ripe it almost crackled with life. The memory had kept him calm, stopped him from sobbing, while some boring minister had waxed on and on about the mercy of God. Frank sat there like a mannequin, numb from losing the love of his life, while Ethan made certain that the appropriate music played, while Andrew's mother and father had sat there like visitors from another planet. Which, come to think of it, they were. Andrew was from Oklahoma or Wyoming, or someplace like that, where "faggot" was simply an insult that straight boys threw at each other. "Faggots" existed only as part of some evil mythology; they weren't real. Andrew had grown up thinking he was the only one of its kind. Now, Andrew was one of the many, another case closed for statistical study.

Brian stopped in front of the mushroom lady. She had a wide blue table covered with piles of mushrooms, from little white buttons up to portobellas the size of salad plates. It was easy to think of her as the mushroom lady. She was a tiny Asian woman, always wearing a big straw hat with a brim that seemed almost as wide as she was tall. She looked just like a mushroom. She bowed slightly when she said hello, as she did now.

"Hello," Brian smiled back at her, always pleased to exchange a smile. He pointed to the little white buttons and said, "A pound of those, please." The mushroom lady took a small plastic bag and filled it halfway, weighed it, and handed it to Brian, smiling and bowing. "Three dollars, please." Brian reached into his pocket and extracted a five, passing it to her over the table, and she reached into her money box and gave him two singles, and another smile and bow. Tucking the plastic bag into his canvas tote, he strolled on, very pleased with the whole exchange. These minute interactions meant so much to him now, now that any errand might be the last time he could make it out of the house.

The funeral would not leave him. As he passed by tables heaped with sweet yellow corn and emerald-green lettuce, he tried to think of something he could do for Frank. Escaping to Mexico for a long weekend, escaping the aftermath of the funeral and the empty-without-Andrew apartment, Frank would be back on Tuesday, and what could he do? Ethan had already cleared out the rented hospital equipment and the clothes. When Frank got back, not only would there be no Andrew, but no trace of Andrew at all. Ethan had confided to Brian that he was going to switch the apartment back to the way Frank had it before Andrew had moved in. That was six years ago. Brian marveled at the passage of time. It felt like another life.

He stopped to admire a plastic bucket packed with marigolds, a dozen different shades of yellow. It was another life. It was the life of reckless good health. He nodded to the man behind the flowers, and moved on. Maybe on the way back.

There was the bread booth. Perhaps he'd get Frank a loaf of sourdough rye, or some pumpernickel? But that, of course, would be calling up the ghost. Andrew had loved to bake bread. He settled on a half dozen egg bagels for himself, put them into his tote bag, and moved on.

Ethan had done a lovely job with the music. Chanticleer, The Kings Singers, things that worked so well in both worlds. The religious choral sound of men's voices, rich and yet simple. So proper, so appropriate to a funeral service. All of it the inside joke, the friends knowing what queer music it was, the family unsuspecting. *Bless Ethan,* Brian smiled to himself, *what would we do without him?*

But we won't ever have to find out. Because he'll be the one putting flowers on our graves and scattering the ashes over the Pacific and calling the families with the bad news. He turned the irony of it over in his mind one more time, how being positive was negative and being negative, well, that was the ticket. And Ethan the only one of the whole bunch to come up on the right side of the test. And he still went and got tested, once every three months, but Brian thought this was pointless superstition. Ethan's love life had, for the past three years, consisted solely of playing mommy to a bunch of sick old men.

He stopped at the honey booth, and took a moment to decide between the orange honey and the clover honey. But we aren't old; we were young, before we all got sick. The little golden tubs of sweetness smiled up at him, but the man he thought of as the beekeeper stayed a wary distance away, the unguarded look on his face openly disgusted with Brian's skeletal appearance. But Brian refused to shrink from this attitude; he only took it as a challenge. Big bright smile, pour on the charm, be a sweet boy and you'll win. He pointed toward the clover honey (knowing not to touch it, fear forming on the beekeeper's face) and asked, "Is that as sweet as the orange honey, or is it just a little darker?" the question plied as if it were an inside joke between the two of them, as if qualities of sweetness and darkness were things that only the two of them really understood. The beekeeper wasn't going to play. "Matter of individual tastes, I'd guess, but if you want sweet, I'd take the orange." Brian paid first, exact change placed on the table between them, took a tub of orange honey, and flashed a smile as he walked away. A few months ago, he might have bristled at the innuendo, but getting angry about it would cost too much energy. And he had wanted sweet, and he was pleased to get it.

And what for Frank? Nothing here seemed to be it. But maybe he would like something sweet. Brian thought of a box of chocolates; he could pick some up on the way home. Chocolate was a college vice, one that Andrew had made Frank give up, as it was allegedly bad for the complexion. A box of chocolates might be just the thing.

The exertion of walking was beginning to strain him, but

he wanted to make one more stop, and buy some herbs. The booth was back toward the entrance anyway, so he made his way back, stopping again to buy some irresistible tomatoes. Great round red globes, color so bright it was dazzling. He had to have some, telling himself it would be a marvelous dose of vitamin C. As he placed them carefully in his bag, he smiled ruefully, remembering when he had loved tomatoes just because they were tomatoes. It was such a bore, this constant strain of thinking of everything as medicine. Mushrooms, honey, tomatoes, there was some scheduled nutritional reason for everything. He thought about buying a box of chocolates and eating them all in one sitting.

Probably kill me, he thought.

He stopped in front of the plants, dozens and dozens of fat, happy little things, basil and oregano and violets and geraniums. Every week, he added one to his windowsill garden, and transplanted the largest to a clay pot on the patio. Most of them did quite well. He had thought, driving over, that he'd like some sage, but he didn't see any on display, so he walked around the outside edge, reading the labels, looking for one that seemed healthy. A tallish, viny kind of thing with little dark green leaves seemed to be the one, although he didn't recognize it. He read the label, and discovered it was thyme.

He pulled out his money and looked for the plant man, who, like the mushroom lady, was always easy to pick out. Usually dressed in several layers of dark green, eyes as bright as blossoms, he had the burnished red cheeks of someone who has spent just the right amount of time in the sun. With a brief hello and a flourish of the potted thyme, he handed two quarters to the plant man, who then put the herb into a small plastic bag and gently explained what it needed. What sort of light, how much water, but

Brian was only half-listening, suddenly overwhelmed by how tired he was.

"I'm sorry," he asked the plant man, "but would you mind writing that down?"

"Oh, sure, no problem, let me get some paper," and he disappeared in the cab of a truck parked nearby. Brian focused on breathing slowly, and remaining upright. *If I can just breathe,* he thought, *I'll be fine. I'll be all right. I'm not all right.*

I'm going to die, this minute, I can't allow this, I'm not going to die, not here, not like this, I'm not going to die, not now, not yet, not now.

When he felt a gentle hand pressing a piece of paper into his palm, and heard a soft inquiry, "Are you okay?" he suddenly was. Focus returned, breath was easy, and he smiled and said, "Yes, thank you, I'm fine, I'll be all right." He believed it, and strolled with a studied amount of casual grace toward the exit, toward the car, thinking, if I can just rest for a moment, then I can make it home.

Getting into the car, he had to consider every movement, unable to call up the forms of habit. Turn the key, he told himself, now pull the handle, put the bag on the seat, every part of it a separate effort. A huge effort. Wondering if he had left too much space between his illness and his death, wondering if he should have killed himself when he had gotten the diagnosis. He looked at his face in the rearview mirror and thought, *I don't have to go on like this. I can just go home and die.* "Not yet," his reflection smiled back at him. "You just bought some thyme."

Turning over the ignition, he decided to go and buy a box of chocolates.

For Frank.

JOHN BARRIOS

The Cradle of His Arms

He never taught me
how to hammer a nail, play
piano, pick-up lines, love.
There is a song he played,
none of the "survived by"
people have heard him play
it. Only Richard. It may be
a requiem for his mother or
a salsa for his saucy wife;
a simple solo for his
not-so-simple sister, perhaps;
"an old cracked tune" for his father,
a man he never mentioned
in my company. I like to believe
his song is for me, a ballad,
a lullaby for an infant age 25.
I would crawl into the cradle of his arms
and he would stroke my head and back
with his musical fingers playing
his lost song on the keyboard of my spine,
humming, lulling me to sleep.
                                        Now
here I am, Richard, at your death-
bed pressing my song along your arms,

whispering my mother's name
into your ear, lips to your
leathery, yellowy skin. Shhh.
Only we can hear, Richard,
you and I.

WASHINGTON S. McCUISTIAN

Molly

Molly found her voice
Silenced by machinery,
Grey-steel lifting heavy
Wooden crates, moving
In great loops.

Molly tells the world,
Without voice, she has
Experienced the great rape,
She has found truth
In youth passing.

Molly spells the word-mounts
Shifting dirt with slate
Finger, pointing out
How ground moves
The way she moved.

Soulstice

Summer's come sticky
as petunia trumpets play
some cheek-puffin' sunny
sassabrass strutting
jazz hot down the
asphalt steaming sip
band ade in the
peach shade swing
trombone water slides
in carnival rhythm
straw hats tipped back
strawberries gone swimming
in lemony sweet sweat's
runnin' down the glass
pucker up
to that horn blow
a breeze easy swaying lovers
drowse in the slumber hum
cicadas be playing
sizzle summertime's come
popsicle bright and winking
like lightning bug tails told
to cool sunburn itching
sting a song, charcoal jazz man
Summer's come
and it's come out to play.

from "The Ugly Duckling"
by Hans Christian Andersen

VIRGINIA DAGGETT

PATRICK ROBBINS

Rope and Wire

"Ready, girls?" Roger called up the stairs. "We're going to be late if you don't hurry up," he said. He tapped the face of his watch with his fingernail for emphasis. Tick tick tick.

"Simmer down, Roger," said Ronda, approaching the stairs with a mug of decaffeinated. "We've got plenty of time."

"If you call them, they will come," Roger said. "Thank you." He took the mug in his large hand and drank. The mug was an old favorite of his; it was white, with a picture of a gravestone on it. Whenever something hot was poured in the cup, the words MY BOSS showed up on the gravestone.

Karyn, fifteen, and Tick, seven, came down the stairs together, dressed in identical white T-shirts and faded jeans. Karyn's T-shirt was tucked in; Tick's had a handprint on it, with a small palm and thumb and long fingers, fingers that stretched from shoulder to belly button.

"Who's been touching you with long fingers?" said Roger, squatting down and tracing the pinkie track.

"They're *my* fingers!" She jumped back and giggled. "I ran 'em 'cross my shirt."

"Let me just get some juice," said Karyn, headed for the fridge.

"Don't drink right out of the carton, Karyn," Ronda called to her daughter.

"And hurry it up," added Roger. He tapped his watch with the bottom of his mug as he straightened up.

"Ticktickttick!" said Tick, giggling. She'd been saying this literally since she could talk and Roger began teaching her time, always tapping his watch. Her first words were "Mama," "Dadda," "rope," "tick," and "Timex."

"Tick tick to you, too," said Roger, looking down.

Ronda came in, buttoning her blouse. The costume showed beneath it as light pink. With a nervous stroke at her thin throat, she asked, "Well, troops, we all set?"

"Let's go," agreed Roger.

"Don't forget your jacket, Tick," Ronda added, putting on a fall coat. "It might be chilly."

"It's in the van. Window seat behind Dad, I call!" She ran for the front door.

"You had it last time!" Karyn yelled after her. She put the orange juice back in the fridge and went over to her parents. There were dark circles under her eyes. She said, "Mom, don't do it if it's going to be windy."

"I didn't say windy, honey, I said chilly. The sun isn't all the way up yet." Ronda kissed her daughter on the cheek. Karyn had to bend her knees slightly to receive the kiss, as her mother was very small. "Don't worry," Ronda said. "Now get in the van."

Karyn straightened and turned to her father.

"No, you can't drive," Roger said immediately. "Not with Tick in the van. Let's go, come on."

"Nobody's going to be there yet," Karyn said in a low voice. She headed to the door and went out into the cold morning air. Roger put on his red windbreaker and kissed the top of his wife's head, and they headed to the garage together to get the pole.

Roger chuckled quietly. "I can read her like a book," he told Ronda confidentially. She said nothing, and he knew she was focusing. He whispered, "Good," as he squatted down and wrapped his hand around the cold steel.

It wasn't easy for Ronda to start tightrope walking. It began when Roger tied a rope between two maple trees in the backyard, then handed his wife an umbrella. By the end of the day she was able to make it halfway across without losing control and having to jump the couple of feet to the ground. Roger was thrilled, saying she had a phenomenal sense of balance and that there was no reason for her not to take full advantage of it.

"It'd be great!" he said over dinner. "This glorious gift you have, and there's a way for everyone in town to see it! We can sell admission into our backyard! Maybe you could do fairs!"

"Dad," said Karyn, "wouldn't Mom be a good dancer?" She refilled her milk glass with orange soda. "Dancers need good balance. Everyone could see her dancing."

"Dancer," said Ronda thoughtfully. She held a forkful of Swiss chard in front of her and looked at it.

Roger looked at Karyn. "That's an idea," he said. "That is definitely an idea. But tell me, princess, which would you rather see? Someone doing the same routines that anyone with training could do, or someone going out and showing themselves to be so special, so unique, so one-of-a-kind, that nobody could follow their lead?" Karyn started to answer, but Tick knocked over her juice cup and the question was forgotten.

Roger began reading more and more about the methods of tightrope walking. He bought his wife a customized pole, explaining to Tick, "It's bent in the middle to lower her center of gravity. That's why it's so long and so heavy, too." He wrote a fan letter to the man who crossed a tightrope between the World Trade Towers and read the reply out loud to the family. He bought a puppy and named it Blondin. He was in the backyard every evening coaching his wife. Karyn was watching from the window the first time she walked all the way across without jumping off. She watched her father lift her mother off the rope and swirl her around the backyard. Her red socks never touched the lawn. That night Roger cooked a celebration spaghetti dinner that was a big success.

It was only twenty miles to the cliff. Karyn had her elbow on the armrest, her head in her palm, eyes closed. Tick bounced around in her seat. Ronda sat back and listened to her husband. "Once Blondin took a stove out with him," he was telling her now. "He took out a stove, cooked an omelet, and ate it, right there on the rope, with Niagara Falls going full blast right below him! That takes a lot of practice," he told her.

Ronda laughed. "I haven't reached that point yet, Roger."

"Well, these things take time," said Roger, tapping out a rhythm on the steering wheel with his fingertips. "He could carry a person piggyback, too. And once he went on stilts."

"Road kill!" Tick called happily from the back. Roger eased into the other lane. The van swept past the mass of innards and matted quills and got in the right lane again. Tick quickly twisted around to look out the back window.

"What a mess," said Ronda.

"They never see it coming," Roger said. "They're so intent on crossing, and whacko." He clapped his hands.

"Ticko!" said Tick.

"Ticko!" said Roger.

"How much further?" Karyn asked, her eyes closed.

"No further at all," Roger said. "We're here."

A van from Channel Nine was the only other vehicle in the parking lot when they pulled in. There was a cameraman at the cliff's edge, filming the rope stretched across the chasm. When he heard the van drive in, he turned the camera and pointed it at them.

"Parking the car on the six o'clock news," said Karyn. "We're famous. Gee, gosh."

"Help your mother with the pole," said Roger. He threw the van into park, shut it off, and tossed the keys back to Karyn without looking. The girls climbed out.

"I'm nervous, Roger," said Ronda. She had her tiny arms folded tightly across her chest. Roger leaned across her to roll up the window, then stroked a massive finger beneath her neck. "You'll be fine," he told her. He unbuckled his seat belt, then hers. "You'll be fine," he said again.

Karyn unlocked the back door, opened it, and put the keys in her pocket. Tick started to pull out one of the pole sections. She gave a high little grunt, and Karyn moved in to help her. The sun was just starting to come over the peaks around the cliff. Two-thirds of the rope was dewy and still in shadow. A couple of birds were on the part in the sunlight, raising and lowering their tail feathers in an effort to keep their balance. Off to the right, about two hundred yards away, two hang gliders were practicing touch-and-go landings. They were dark silhouettes against the sky. Farther off a flock of seagulls searched for breakfast.

"Don't disturb your mother," Roger always told the girls about a half-hour before the lessons were to begin. "She's getting ready. Don't disturb her."

Karyn soon came to understand that "disturbing" her mother meant breaking her concentration. Nothing could be brought up that did not relate to tightrope walking. By extension, this meant that only Roger could talk to her. "You should never let go of the pole," Karyn would hear through the door of the study. "The pole is your friend and it can save your life. No matter what happens, hold on to the pole." And she would go upstairs and wait until dusk, when her mother would be finished walking the tightrope out back.

Karyn watched her mother practice in the beginning. She and Tick would stand at the sliding glass door and watch her on the rope, taking heel-to-toe steps. Roger stood on the ground, taking shuffling sidesteps, arms halfway out to catch her.

"Perfect!" he'd say. "Now, backwards."

One night he brought home a videotape of great circus performers. After the jugglers and the trapeze artists and the human cannonballs, the tightrope walkers came on the screen. One of the tightrope walkers was a poodle. A purple poodle with white roots stood on the rope, wavering back and forth, its dark eyes open wide. A yellow pole was balanced on the backs of its front paws. It tottered forward a couple of steps, then craned its neck to the side and stared at Karyn from the TV screen. "Yip," it said. Karyn got up and went to her room.

She never watched her mother practice in the backyard

again. Tick stood at the dirty sliding glass door every night, peering at the tottering figure in the dusk, but Karyn never stood there with her. She felt bad about that, and one night she decided to tell her mother why she'd turned away. She thought about what she could say as she went down the stairs to her parents' room. Nothing came to mind right away, and Karyn could only hope that the words would spill out naturally once she began talking.

She found her mother in the kitchen, elbows on the Formica counter, fingertips pressing temples. Roger was there too, standing behind her, arms around her, speaking gently into her ear. "Never hurry those last steps," he was saying. "Many people have died only a few steps away from land because they were in a hurry to get there. Slow and steady wins the race." He kissed her behind the earlobe. Karyn turned and went back upstairs.

"We're here with Roger Banner," said the short, fat man in the Channel Two blazer. "Roger, you've been planning this crossing for how long?"

"Well, you might stay it's been in the stages for several years now," Roger said. "I decided this year to leave my job so I could take over my wife's career and be her manager. We've been working toward this crossing since then, step by step. In fact," he said, "you could say our handling of her career is a perfect parallel for her career." He smiled.

"Why tightroping?" the short, fat man asked.

"I've always loved the circus," Roger reported. "I think everyone does at some level. And for me, the tightrope was the biggest thrill of all. The outcome is always in doubt, and it's drawn out. Not like the trapeze, which is over in an instant. So at the end the payoff is that much greater."

"Did you ever consider trying it?"

"Tightroping? Good heavens, no. I don't have the look you need. My wife has it, but I don't."

"Where's your wife now, Roger?" The short, fat man was beginning to sweat under the lights. He wiped his brow with the back of the hand he was holding the mike in, then quickly brought it back up to Roger's level.

". . . van getting herself ready. She'll be wearing a bright-red outfit with stars on it. The Star-Spangled Banner." He had thought up this name himself. Tick liked it. Karyn thought it extremely corny and threatened to use Ronda's maiden name for the rest of her unmarried life. Ronda, who had final say, went along with it. "She'll be a symbol for what makes this country great, what this country is all about," Roger said. "I already know what she's made of, and so do the kids. It's time for everyone else to know, too."

"And speaking of the kids, here they are now." He turned and lowered his Channel Two mike. "Say hi to the folks at home," he said.

"Hi, folks at home," said Karyn. "We're more than halfway to our goal. Keep sending us your money."

"Hi, Kristen!" said Tick. "That's my friend from school."

"How do you feel about your mother going out over this drop of one-tenth of a mile, with only a rope between her and the ground?"

"Is one-tenth big?" asked Tick.

Karyn looked directly into the black eye of the camera. "I don't like to see my mom risking her life. You do what you have to, I suppose, if you're going to survive. It's just a drag that we're all surviving on account of her doing this.

It's too much surviving for one person to be responsible for."

Behind her, Roger raised his wrist to eye level and tapped it. The short, fat man quickly wound up and the lights were turned off with several loud clicks.

"Ticktickticklick!" Tick yelled.

"That guy was sweeeaaat-*ing*," Karyn said with a little smile. "I'm surprised he didn't short the mike out."

"Karyn," Roger said, "that was no way to talk about your mother." Behind him, the hang gliders circled.

"What?" Karyn protested. "All I said was I'm really worried when she goes out there." She put her left hand up on her left shoulder and began tugging her shirt collar. Roger looked at the circles under her eyes.

"You're still tired," he told her. "Okay, let's go over to the next one." The three of them walked over to the white Channel Eleven van, where a man with rimless glasses, a walrus mustache, and a microphone stood waiting for them.

Karyn wasn't all that surprised when Roger got fired. She never thought he was cut out for the publishing business to begin with. He'd also been taking sick days off to help Ronda train, and they'd added up. So when he called everyone around the table and announced that they'd be leading a whole new life starting this very night, Karyn asked, "Are we going to stop throwing away the want ads?"

"Don't get cute," said Roger. "No, we're going to let your mother be the breadwinner in this family. If anyone can do it, she can." He leaned way down and gave Ronda a peck on the cheek.

Tick asked, "How will she win bread?"

"Your mother is going to become a professional tightrope walker. We'll make a big splash so everyone will know her name, and then we'll be fending off the offers!" His voice grew louder and stronger. "She can hit the talk shows, she can be on TV specials, maybe even get some kind of movie deal! Get a quick book on her life written up, I can use my connections—"

Karyn interrupted. "Dad, that's four or five chickens that haven't hatched yet."

"Your mother's the hen that can hatch them. What, are you looking for trouble?"

Karyn looked at Ronda. She was kneading her lower lip with her upper one, making her mouth even smaller. Her eyes were downcast, and she was briskly stroking Roger's fingers, which were at her elbow. Karyn looked at her father and said, "Not me."

"Good. Now, in a few months your mother is going to make her professional debut."

The sun was mostly out now, and the crowd was getting bigger. By ten minutes of nine there were well over eighty people milling about. Many of them were watching the hang gliders. One did a loop-the-loop, and there was applause.

"Stupid hang gliders," said Roger after the Channel Eleven man was finished and had left. "Don't they know they're taking away from your mother's concentration?"

"I think they're neat," said Tick.

Karyn watched them swoop and soar. "I wonder what it is that makes people want to step off cliffs," she said thoughtfully.

"Well, let's go get your mother," Roger said, and the three of them walked to the van. The tar scraped against the soles of their shoes, as they walked to the passenger side of the van.

"Honey?" Roger said, and opened the door. Ronda was in the passenger seat with her eyes closed and the seat belt fastened. Her red leotard shone limply in the sun. The stars caught some of the rays and flashed them back. She had designed the costume, and Roger had given it his enthusiastic approval.

Roger gently tapped his watch. Tick tick. "Ready, honey?" he asked her.

She opened her eyes and smiled up at him. "Ready as I'll ever be," she said firmly. She unbuckled and got out of the car. Karyn and Tick brought the pole over to her. Fully attached, it weighed thirty pounds and was twice as long as she was tall. Ronda took it and bent down to kiss Tick. She went on tiptoe to kiss Karyn. She held Roger for a long moment.

The Channel Eleven camera was pointed at them. The cameraman was adjusting his lens; the soundman had his microphones at the ready. "You guys getting all this?" Karyn asked them sharply. Ronda turned, swinging the pole. It hit nobody, but Channel Eleven backed up all the same. "Sorry!" Roger called to the man. Then, to his wife, "Focus." She nodded and walked to the cliff's edge. Her family walked behind her. People made way for her. Photographers took her picture. The hang gliders duked it out. At nine-o-three, Ronda Banner reached the cliff's edge, breathed in, and took her first step onto the rope. Then her second step. The crossing had begun.

"She is too!" Tick said to her sister.

It was the night before the crossing. Karyn pulled the covers over her head.

"You haven't even been watching her practice," Tick

continued. "I have. She's gotten really, really good. Daddy doesn't even hold his arms out anymore."

It was true. Their father had taken to trying to distract her while she was on the rope. "Watch out!" he would yell. Or, "What's that?" Or, "Don't fall!" When the neighbors complained about the noise, he lobbed beanbags at her. Soon nothing short of an explosion could break her concentration.

"Does he make her do any tricks?" Karyn asked from beneath the blankets.

"Only one," came Tick's muffled voice. "It's not anything big. Daddy says the real tricks will come later. But she's really good at going back and forth."

It was hot under the covers. Karyn tossed them off and breathed the night air.

"The rope is really wide, too. It's two and a quarter inches wide. My foot is almost as wide as that!" Tick held up her foot for emphasis.

Karyn resisted the urge to tickle it. Instead, she repeated, "She's not ready, Tick."

"She is too!" Tick insisted.

"Kids!" their father called from downstairs. "Your mother's got a big day tomorrow, she needs her sleep—keep it quiet."

They fell silent. Karyn waited for some form of exhaustion. Before Tick's breathing became deep and regular, Tick whispered one last time, "Is too."

"Does she do any tricks?" whispered a man in a Channel Two blazer.

"One," Roger whispered back, his eyes not leaving his wife. She was now more than halfway across. "She does it on the way back."

"Let us know when."

The crowd was quiet. The whirring of the cameras was the only sound. Roger, squatting in front of the rope, rubbed his nose. He yanked at it. *Is an itchy nose good luck or bad?* he wondered. It was one or the other, he knew that. Tightroping wasn't pure skill; there was always a little luck involved. But the less luck that was needed, the better.

Only about twenty steps more to go now. Ronda was taking it very slowly, heel to toe. There was no hurry.

A light breeze brushed Karyn's cheek, and she stiffened. Her mother showed no effects. The pole gave her stability. She was almost to the end now. It was totally silent. Tick had her hands clasped beneath her chin, and was rocking back and forth. Even the hang gliders had left the sky and were now all on the cliff, watching.

Three more unrushed steps and Ronda rested her foot on land. Behind her, the crowd roared and horns honked. Tick jumped up and down, and Karyn switched to chewing the nails on her left hand. Roger knelt at the cliff's edge and waited.

She turned and smiled, tense, exhausted, and partly relieved all at once. Then she set her face, put forth her tiny foot, and pressed it onto the rough rope. The crowd quickly hushed again, and she put forth her other foot and began the crossing back. Now the crowd could see her face, a study of concentration.

Roger began to smile. He had never before permitted himself to smile while his wife was on the rope. There was always the chance that she might forget everything he had told her in the safety of the backyard. But she was walking very slowly, even when close to land. She was totally focused on her work, her face so set, so intent on what she did. Roger raised his hand and gestured to the news crew; she was about to do her trick. They moved closer to the cliff's edge.

Ronda was at the middle of the rope, and now she stopped. She moved her hands closer and closer together, until the sides of her pinkies were touching, right at the pole's center. Then she removed one hand, her right. She raised it to the crowd and waved. The crowd applauded uncertainly, then gaining conviction.

"That's the trick?" the short, fat man from Channel Two asked.

"Don't you get it?" Roger whispered. " 'O'er the land of the free'?"

The fat man mopped his brow. "I wish she'd smile more."

Then Roger saw the hang gliders.

The night before the crossing, Karyn dreamed that her father shot the purple poodle with white roots in front of the Channel Five news team, who turned to the camera and intoned, "Roger Banner. A gentle man living in a crazy world." She woke up with a start. Tick snored lightly across the room.

Karyn tossed off her blankets and sat up. Her mother would be sleeping in the guest room, so as to be separate from the rest of the family, free of distraction. The floor creaked under Karyn's feet as she got out of bed and tiptoed out of the room.

Light seeped out under the guest room door. Karyn lightly brushed her knuckles against the door, then let herself in. Her mother was sitting Indian-style in the middle of the bed, eyes closed. Her slight, sad smile was framed by the twitching corners of her mouth.

"Mom?"

"Close the door, Karyn," she whispered. Karyn closed it, then scurried to the bed. She got on and put her arms around her mother. The mattress sagged beneath her knees. She said, "You don't have to go, Mom."

"Karyn," she said. Her voice was low, smooth, without any ripples. "I want to go."

Karyn's arms, still around her mother, went cold. "Why?" she squeaked.

Ronda sucked in a breath, her tiny cheekbones accentuated for a moment. "Oh, God, Karyn, I hope you can understand this." She leaned back, looked into her daughter's huge pupils, and began. "For me, Karyn, the rope is safety. It's not a wire I'm walking on, but a rope. The rope has give to it that the wire doesn't. The rope can't cut you. The rope has texture, it has warmth that wire could never have. Karyn, your father is a wire."

Karyn tried to picture a strand of wire that weighed 245 pounds.

"I love him dearly, but he's a wire. And there's always the danger that if I do something, he'll cut me without meaning to. When I'm on the rope, he can't cut me. You know? It's the rope and me, together. Everyone else is only watching, but we're doing. They're all passive, and we're active, the rope and I. It's the only time I can be in control of everything." She coughed lightly. "I do have to thank your father for getting me into this, really. Because when I'm on the rope, I can be . . ." She started tapping the air, searching for the right word.

"You can be?" asked Karyn.

Ronda stopped tapping the air and looked at her daughter. Very, very softly, she said, "Go to sleep now, Karyn."

"Mom—"

She smiled. "I'll be seeing you in the morning."

The hang gliders were dressed all in white. One glider was also blue; the other was white with a burst of a rainbow on it. They trailed banners behind them. REED ACADEMY RULES, read the one attached to the blue glider. TOLD YOU WE'D DO IT CYNDI!! read the other.

The person on the white glider waved to the crowd at the cliff's edge, where the cameras were. The glider, its balance thrown off, began to nose-dive, and the pilot gave a startled yelp that bounced off the canyon walls.

Scattered people began to shout warnings, but Ronda gave no indication of hearing them. The white glider sliced down toward her.

With a supreme effort, the pilot regained control, brought the nose up, and barely skimmed over Ronda's head, actually brushing a sneakered toe through her hair. The rope jounced and swayed. A woman screamed. Quickly, Ronda threw herself down to grab the rope with her right hand and scissored her legs around it behind her. With her left hand she held the pole. It pulled her, spun her so that her back faced the distant ground. More people were screaming now, or shouting. Only the Channel Two camera followed the progress of the hang gliders as they soared off. The other two stayed with the drama of the main event.

"Ronda!" Roger shouted. "The pole!"

Tick was crying. Karyn scooped her up quickly and turned to her father. "Dad, I'm taking Tick home."

Roger barked, "What!" His eyes never left his wife. "You can't abandon your mother like this!"

"Let her be, Dad."

"You're too young to drive anyway," he said distractedly.

"I know how, though. And we're going."

"You're not going any—" He grabbed her forearm just as Ronda let out a cry. It was the first sound she had made on the rope. It was an awful sound. Roger let go of Karyn as though she were on fire. She withdrew her hand, which held the keys, and ran into the crowd, jangling.

One of the stars on Ronda's costume was scraped off, and it began to fall. Two more followed. They swayed, fluttered, spun end over end, spiraled. It seemed they could not decide just exactly how to fall. One camera was pointed at Roger, to capture his reaction. "The pole!" he shouted again. There was a screech of brakes behind him, then a loud motor revving. Ronda, holding the rope close, cried out again. Roger couldn't believe this was all happening.

LISA LINN KANAE

Blue

There are days, still,
when I must look up towards the Koolau mountains
to feel the familiar smell of rain falling on
eucalyptus and ginger growing wild

and fragile at the edge of the watershed mark.
We shared a life there once,
in a home painted forest-green with wide
empty windows trimmed white.

Blades of sunlight pierced the silent rooms,
cast a glare across the glass covering
a photograph in a gold-tone frame;
two young lovers clutching white roses,
laughter and lace blurred by layers of dust.

Outside in the open tool shed
I thought you were busy tinkering with old lamps,
a broken lawn mower engine, furniture fragments,
until I found used syringes, empty plastic amber vials,
needle bruises on your hips.
Days pushed into months,
milligram after milligram,
lie after lie, every promise as empty
as the vials you tossed aside,
like your wife, used up and left behind.
I could no longer see myself in your vacant eyes.

And I wonder now,
how you recognized in that pile of cobweb
covered lumber a porch swing.
Unraveling chains like Christmas ribbons,
it was your last gift to me.
You smeared rust and sweat on your T-shirt,
like chocolate icing on a napkin as white
as the clouds over the Koolaus.
You held your hand out to me, palm faced up
as if waiting for rain to wash away the fragile webs.

You painted that porch swing blue;
like the sky above the Koolaus.
There are days, still,
when I feel the mountains
watching over me.

Bldg C Girls' Restroom

First I suck on a menthol filter tip,
then release Kool rings, swirling soundless to
pacify the woman-child in the mirror,
whose sable wide-eyes
dart side to side.

Maybeline lashes beat like rabbit breaths,
eyelids powdered baby-blue with a sponge tipped wand.
Bite the unsure lower-lip lacquered with
a sticky cherry gloss.
Am I perfect yet?
Please remember me anyway.

My black felt tip flaws the gray tiled blocks
arranged like the halls outside; single file, side-by-side.
Straight paths lead to straight minds.
Here. Straighten this—

lopsided hearts, anonymous threats,
crude poetry dedicated to the boy with the senior-prom
    tuxedo

that matched my pink polyester dress,
never to be worn again.
Once white-gloved high at the elbows, these hands
will mark this wall well.

Ink, dry before the bell rings,
before the shiny gowns and tasseled squares are worn.
I peel the cigarette in the bone porcelain ashtray,
which was once a bathroom sink,
where water will wash away the ashes.

CAROLINE C. REICH

A coolness like a moonbeam spectral star
It teaches us we know we think we are
We wonder what we sense and sensing seem
To exist outside a word a fall a dream
A hole a gap a loss we seem to say
Will if we once ignore it go away
If only we could know it's no such thing
Instead we squander all for one last fling
The constant battle, voices in the night
Could if we were prepared or if we might
Accept it, tell us what we need to know
About the final obstacle, but no,
If once we saw it, it would never be
As it had been, nor of course would we.

ANNE RILEY

Hazards of the Road

I was dreaming of perfection again. Cruising down a country road in the rain. Tired rain. It had fallen all day and by midnight when I stepped behind the wheel it was lazy, dropping leisurely through the fog carrying wispy leaves to stir across the shiny pavement. Autumn had sighed its last. Nothing left to do but rake it up, light a match, and fill the air with musty smoke.

Perfection is a useful dream when the job is a job, the house is a lonely mess, and the long drive between offers no surprises. Especially after a night of schmoozing potential clients. I work for an interior design firm specializing in corporate accounts. I'd spent all evening wining and dining the operations manager of an investment firm—Beckworth & somebody—and their smug Chicago architect. Between the investor's ulcer stories and the architect's advances the evening had been a bust. It was the business dream: my own shop, the loft office, brick walls, windows on three sides, a client marveling at my expertise, writing a fat check, the advance for turning her mildewed basement into an upscale pool room. I was reaching for the fabric samples on the top shelf of a unit framed by Grecian columns, building her up with details of the special qualities of the new Italian linens, when a doe stepped onto the shoulder of the road. I braked, remembering too late the concept of skid, on a wet road, at fifty.

The tail end of my Honda took the deer down as it spun. The tires and I screamed in unison until the car jolted to a stop perpendicular to the road, leaving sudden silence and, when I remembered to breathe, the sound of steady dripping rain.

"Damn." An ache in my shoulder spread to my chest when I reached for the door handle. I flipped on the hazards and stepped out into the wet night. I moved slowly through the insistent beams of the headlights, took a deep breath, and tiptoed the length of my car. She was alive beating a steady rhythm against the gravel of the shoulder with the hoof of her unbroken foreleg, looking at me or at nothing with a limpid frightened eye. Her other front leg jutted out as if from her belly, her hind legs lay limp, a muscle in the upturned haunch twitched like a nervous liar, and there was a bloody smear across the white fur of her belly. I knelt in the gravel and she started with the instinct to run. I stroked her head and began a quiet litany of comfort words. She was warm and surprisingly dry. I wanted to take her, all two hundred pounds of her, into my arms to warm and quiet her. I wanted her to live, but it was clear she wasn't going to live. I wanted a gun.

When I was a child, about eight, my father left my sister and me with our grandparents one fall day while he went hunting. I don't remember where my mother was. It was dark when he came for us and when Grandpa asked if he'd made his kill he led us out to the car in the driveway. He reached under the bumper to loosen the twine that held the trunk lid, threw back a frayed quilt, and stood aside to let us look. The young buck, frozen with rigor mortis, filled the trunk. My little sister, Kate, stepped forward and touched the hoof that rested on the lip of the trunk at the end of a stiff golden leg. Her eyes brimmed with tears and when Dad asked what was wrong she said, "Daddy, put him out in the woods now and let him run away, okay?" We gave the meat to charity and my father locked up his rifles and didn't hunt again until we were grown. It was a lost memory, completely forgotten until I knelt beside the dying doe.

Gravel clung to my shins when I pulled myself up. The ache had grown more insistent and my left knee felt huge and stiff. I popped the trunk and rummaged for the tire iron, wondered if I was strong enough to crush her skull. The tire iron was too short and too light. I bent into the front seat, books, briefcase, pocketknife, lipstick—not one tool of destruction. Except me. And my car. I limped back to the doe, her eye now an unfocused mirror of shock, kissed her between her bristly ears, and murmured my guilt. Then I made my way back to the driver's seat, belted myself in, backed onto the road, kept backing until I had thirty yards running room, and popped the clutch. There was just enough time for second thoughts before the impact bounced my wreck into the left lane. I cranked up The Stones, jammed into fifth gear, and drove like the devil was hitching a ride on my bumper.

At home I poured whiskey, loaded Lyle Lovett, Nirvana, and The Cure into the CD player, and hit the random button. I filled a plastic grocery bag with ice for my knee, fell into a chair at the kitchen table, and hoisted the bad leg onto another. The cat sat in the doorway and looked warily from me to the speakers in the next room where Lyle crooned, "I know you know . . ." I tried to call her to me,

"Here kitty kitty, here Tig," but it was like she knew. Like some kind of animal collective unconscious had alerted her to the fact that I'd killed one of her own.

I don't drink much anymore, let alone whiskey. The bottle was a Christmas Eve gift from my brother-in-law, a drink-with-me drunk, but I needed the singe and I needed the buzz. Mostly I wanted the numbness of incoherence. Between sips I held the glass up to the light and admired the warm amber glow. Perfect deerskin brown.

RACHAEL Y. BANNING

Deer Season

You cluster on the
sides of the road
like teeming ants—
all hoping to bring home the "big one."
In your camouflage
and gaudy reflectors
you expect to hide
from your prey.
As you stealthily make your way
into the forest
little do you know
they have fled to

safer ground,
having smelled your
dooming scent.

KIMBERLY GREENFIELD

Flight

Skin kite drawn tightly
against shoulder blades sailing
over river maps you drew
with fingers on my back.
I hunted long
for clues of you hidden
in worn water paths,
tore through tattered
bed sheets black
to find your body stone.
I charged white rapids,
the arch of my hip
torn kite tails
tangled on jagged edges
of winter rocks.
Trapped, I found you waiting,
beckoning to doves,
your blue eyes delicately

preened like their wings,
permanent tears below your eyelids.
You never look down
to catch my pale face
in your shadow. You don't see
how it covers me
like wet moss
and sticks like stains of tears
that never dry.
I plead with you
to tear yourself
from your feathered perch.
You look only to the circled sky
and hold out your hands
calmly to catch
the last of your silent doves.

GEORGE CARNER

The Pond

It was Derek Lake who got Catherine pregnant. On this same pullout couch on which she now sat, in the tiny living room that barely fit it when it was opened up. She stared at the television in front of her, seeing but not watching, thinking of the trouble she was in. She leaned to the end of the couch to peer past the wall and down the short hallway to the kitchen. The two hands on the clock that hung above the kitchen table formed a narrow V. Five past eleven. She wasn't tired. She had grown accustomed to being awake while her mother worked the graveyard shift at the hospital. Catherine would tread lightly around the small house until eight, when her mother rose and began her fastidious program of preparing herself to leave. At eight-o-five the light in her bedroom would snap on, then the light to the bathroom across the hall. The two paths of light would converge on the carpet between the rooms, like a wide balance beam for a clumsy gymnast, and her mother moved back and forth across it. Appearing in the hall in increasing stages of readiness, Catherine's mother reminded her of a time-worn parody of the paper dolls she dressed as a child, in the damp basement of that same house. Catherine still slept in the basement, with her little sister, Liz, within the same cheap, wood-paneled walls.

The house was set on a small peninsula at the edge of a pond and in the spring, when the water rose, it knocked right at the back door, which was sealed shut, and would let itself in, squeezing through the cracks in the foundation, soaking the basement floor, and flooding it with an odor that made Catherine think of rotting vegetables. It was fall, and the water would be frozen soon. Boys would be out on the pond soon, wielding sticks and tearing wide gashes in the ice with their heavy skates. Derek Lake, who got Catherine pregnant, would be among them.

Catherine knew it was Derek because when she found out how long she was carrying, the date of conception hovered over the middle of a two-week stretch when there was only Derek. She imagined that she could remember the very night, but she didn't try to convince herself of it. She laughed at the girls who did that. She remembered how pathetic her friend Megan had sounded during a false alarm when she said that it just had to have happened the night Bobby had taken her to the Candlelight Motel. "It just had to have happened then." Catherine had also been to the Candlelight, where the rooms, made to simulate the atmosphere of a cave, were available for ten dollars an hour. So Catherine remembered, but not to stick a flag in the dirt of that night, or give it an undeserved sanctity. She remembered it because that night had changed her somehow.

The night she was thinking of was a warm one in the beginning of October, and felt to her like a flashback of summer. An hour had passed since her mother left for work that night, and Catherine had still not heard the shift of the screen frame from her mother's room. Entering through her mother's bedroom was Derek's idea. The peninsula was shared by Mrs. Roulier, a surveillance camera with spectacles, who only appeared outside her house to offer critique or enlighten Catherine's mother to any "funny business" that was going on while she was out. So Derek suggested the low window on the other side of the house where the pond bent into a small wooded gulf. "I can get in there easy," he told her, as if he considered it less of a physical challenge than the front door. That sentence stuck in Catherine's mind as the perfect thing for a boy to say, a boy who knows what the prize will be. She fancied that if he had to climb over a barbed-wire fence to get in, he would still use the word "easy."

Catherine had grown impatient. Derek was always dangerously prompt. Catherine wondered if it was a hormonal eagerness or if he simply liked the sense of risk he got by slashing across the street behind her mother's taillights, like a careless rodent. The disruption of his predictability was making her nervous. Catherine walked to the kitchen and pulled a bottle down from her mother's stash from above the sink. She put two ice cubes in a glass and poured in a thick pool of vodka. The ice snapped, expanding against the warmth of the liquor.

She hated screwdrivers. The vodka made the orange juice taste hot and rancid. She didn't know why, but she felt like she needed them now, the same way she sometimes needed coffee, or cigarettes. It was funny to her, the kinds of things she needed, for no apparent reason.

She went back to the living room and sat Indian-style on the couch, tugging her nightshirt down, dragging a fingernail on her bare leg. She looked around the room as if it were the first time she'd seen it with the light on. The room was crammed with tiny furniture that collapsed or was interchangeable, as if in that room were the possibility to imitate every room in the house. A cherry-wood table that concealed a set of TV tables beneath it, two foldout chairs, the pullout couch. She looked at the walls, covered with oil paintings of slipshod seascapes, and at the entertainment center, on the shelf beside the TV, populated with a dense fleet of photographs of herself and of her sister, their successions of age scattered about them. As she drank, Catherine began to feel relaxed, remote, dimly excited, and full of a sense of herself as a young woman. She was becoming very aware of the first slights of sophistication brought by alcohol and a late lover. She began to think of Derek's lateness as a coyness, a tease. Maybe he was watching TV, taking a nap, taking his time. It never crossed her mind that he would not show up. She considered the qualities she possessed which gave her pride: pretty green eyes, a body she was proud of, smart enough to stay away from entangling relationships.

Catherine played games. One night she ran and locked the window of her mother's bedroom when she left for work. She turned off the lights, and when Derek arrived she hid her face in the blinds of the living-room window beside her mother's room. Derek circled the house slowly, throwing pebbles at the panes and hissing her name. Catherine shrank back from the window, laughing. Finally he cursed and threw a rock hard off the side of the house, and when she heard him start to walk away she swallowed her laughter, and pulled herself up to the window. "Derek, wait," she said. She felt bad that she had used him for a joke that way, but she had to hold down her laughter again, seeing how angry he looked because something was being kept from him.

Catherine had gotten the bottle of vodka and the carton of orange juice from the kitchen and set them on the rug, beside the couch to save her trips. She had been watching PBS—a nature show was on describing the nesting habits of a bird that dwelled atop coastal cliffs—when she heard the screen shoot up in her mother's room, and it was like someone had hit a switch inside her, generating an electric anticipation that hummed through her, bringing her back to real life, real movement. She saw the dark back of his head ducking into the hallway. Just then he looked like a burglar making sure that what he was after was unguarded.

"Hello. Over here," she said loudly, waving the hand not holding a drink at him. He swiveled his head toward her, quickly, and his eyebrows were up as if he were surprised to find her there.

"It's late, I thought you'd be sleeping or something," he said, smirking, and came into the room. He stood there, looking at her up and down, his hands in his pockets. He was sizing her up, she knew, with his eyes, and it made her uneasy.

The alcohol had drained from her head and had withdrawn to her stomach, making her queasy. She felt more comfortable naked, against him, with no room for observation.

She put her drink on the cherry-wood beside the couch, and pulled her nightshirt down, pinning it to the couch with her thumbs. He looked from her to the TV and she watched his profile. His skin was pale, but healthy, with burning red blotches high up on his cheeks. She thought, *he must have run here,* because she only saw those blotches when she watched him play hockey, or sometimes after sex. His face was boyish and handsome, she thought. His mouth was permanently parted, and always seemed on the verge of smiling or laughing. His eyebrows were furrowed in curiosity, a soft, joking look of scrutiny that she'd seen on him before, whenever he was seeing something new or strange.

Derek sat next to her on the couch, and let out a sound that was half-grunt, half-sigh. He came down with a heavy thump that shook the floor and betrayed the usual pretense of respect he normally showed for the house when he came. The way he usually stood, looking around the room, sitting down carefully, quietly, trying to be humorous, gentlemanly, trying to create the illusion of reverence, all seemed so funny to Catherine now that he had abandoned it. She laughed inwardly, at the way he had revealed himself, because she had known it was an act, a prop he used to uphold his own image of innocence and chivalry.

Her laugh reverberated inside her, and leaked out. She didn't know if the thump in the floor would ever stop reverberating out of the couch, back and forth through the house and out onto the wide pond, making a million tiny waves and ripples there.

"What's so funny?" Derek asked, as he watched her from the corner of his eye.

"Nothing, nothing," she said, still laughing, shaking her head, and then, "you."

"Me?" he asked. "You've been knocking back a little too much of that sauce I think."

Catherine stopped laughing and looked at the rug. The rubber bottoms on the legs of the bed frame had made two small circles on the rug, and Catherine wondered if her mother had noticed them. A long time passed with nothing said. It was awkward and uncomfortable, as if neither she nor Derek knew the next move, as if because of the time, the normal routine did not apply. Catherine turned to her drink, still full, and picked it up, looking into it through the glass, a murky orange and yellow. She took a menacing gulp, as if she were trying to hit something in her stomach very hard.

Derek was still watching. She had swallowed too much. The alcohol was churning inside her, scorching her throat and glazing her eyes. "Ah, how refreshing," she said in a hoarse whisper, looking back at him.

He laughed and said something about AA to her, but that was all she caught. She felt a wave of dizziness. The water in her eyes was fuzzing her vision as she tried to look at the television. She needed something bright to focus on, but the image on the TV danced in front of her, escaping through the shield of liquid. She heard Derek speaking, but it sounded like it was coming from another place, like a voice over a telephone. "Now repeat after me," he was saying slowly, "my name is Cathy Harris, and I'm an alcoholic."

Catherine was drunk and so tired now that every organ in her body, every bone and muscle and layer of skin, took on its own separate weight and combined like magnets to pull her down.

She thought of her mother at work, bustling in and out of rooms, down the clean, fluorescent-lit halls, white from her shoulders to her rubber-soled shoes. She pictured her smiling at patients, filling them with drugs. Her mother had her own cache in the medicine cabinet. Percodan, Xanax, Valium were her mother's friends, which she invited in like a secret, amiable congregation into her bloodstream. Catherine didn't care though—at least it had kept her mother from interfering with her life.

"I'm so tired, I have to go to sleep," Catherine said, pulling her warm hands over her face and into her hair. Catherine was nauseous, groping toward sleep, hoping she looked to Derek as worn as she felt.

It hadn't worked the way she had wanted, none of it. She had been excited when Derek arrived, but sensed now that even then her desire had been waning. The time crept up on her, and the booze, and they were threatening to revolt.

She looked for the TV again but couldn't find it. The only light remaining was from the hot bulb on the ceiling which was hurled at her for a moment as Derek pulled her to her feet, painfully, by her arms. She slumped hard against the wall, and her lids so heavy, like toothless bear traps she fought to keep from snapping shut, or like the heavy iron doors she'd seen in movies, closing off the entrance to the castle.

Then the light was off and she was flat on her back with the moon glowing on her through the screen of the open window behind the couch. His weight wasn't on her yet, but she didn't know what she'd do when it was. She was sure she would puke. His hands were on her, his knees at her sides. His touch helped a little. Maybe he was trying to bring her awake. His hands were cool like the breeze off the pond was cool, and the moonlight. She opened her eyes to look at him. He was smiling. His skin was blanched by the moon. She thought he looked busy, as if he were doing a job. Catherine struggled to keep her stomach down.

She felt the spark, a coarse, dry, hot feeling inside her that made her think of someone trying to start a fire by rubbing two sticks together. With a gush Derek Lake was inside her. Her stomach threatened to lurch again as he lowered his weight onto her. She felt suffocated, she wanted to crawl backward out the window, to propel herself out from under him and into the dark pond. She wanted to do the backstroke, to move her limbs freely through the deep, yielding water, to breath air other than what he sent down to her.

She began to drift off over the rhythm of the steel bedsprings, groaning beneath the mattress. She started to think of when she was a little girl, Liz's age, sitting on the shores of the pond in the summer, by herself. She had always thought she was so much more beautiful when she was alone. She would sit admiring her knees, thought she had such perfect knees, and her forearms, the sun making her hair warm.

Catherine's crotch and inner thighs were becoming lubricated by Derek's sweat. The sweat collected in the hollows of her thighs, catching the breeze at intervals, giving her a chill, soothing her. She began to think of when Derek had taken her virginity on this couch. She had been fourteen. She remembered not knowing how to stop him, or exactly why she was supposed to. It had lasted half a minute and when he left she threw away the sheets after staring at them forever. Then she went to sleep.

She thought about things that happened since then, how she learned things. Like this guy Keith, who she heard was married now. He had taken her to his apartment and shown her how to do 69. She wondered why she did such things. She couldn't remember how the opportunities had arisen. She thought now that Derek probably wouldn't have just let her go to sleep even if she had pleaded. Pleading wouldn't help; he would do what he wanted. She knew that. Derek had told her once that she had no morals, or someone else had told her he said it, and maybe he was right. She hadn't cared what she did or what was done to her, but she had never felt the revulsion of feeling helpless to stop it. Now, her stomach was crawling past her lungs.

Derek let out a scream. She opened her eyes, thinking he was finished, then saw her own hands dug into the flesh of his arms above the elbows. "Oh god, I'm so sorry, Derek," she said. When she dropped her hands there were little fingernail imprints in his arms, like half-moons. "I didn't realize I was doing it."

She forced a tiny, self-conscious giggle, trying to make him think her violence was driven by some unfathomable, uncontrollable pleasure. "Just be careful," he said. He started to shove against her again. She had been lying still but now she was meeting his thrusts, pulling him in as if to overpower him, trying to make him finish. Her eyes burned, her limbs ached, and the dull fire between her legs was spreading, blistering her. She didn't remember when he left that night, only her exhaustion and relief, and the caress of the breeze through the window. She felt burnt entirely and left to smolder in the stark white ashtray of the pull-out couch.

That was the last time she had slept with Derek Lake or with anyone. She hadn't hid by the window anymore when Derek came to the house at night, but sat on the couch or at the kitchen table with the shades pulled, and maybe let out a small sigh, and was thankful for the locks on the windows. She ignored Derek whenever she saw him around, more like avoided him, stayed out of his path.

As of tonight, she calculated, it had been five weeks since the night he must have impregnated her, at least two weeks since she had last heard pebbles pitched at the windows. Catherine rubbed her stomach gently underneath her shirt. "Old habits are hard to break," she thought, and laughed a little, happy to be putting distance between herself and those events. She felt as if she were drifting out to sea on a boat, a small but sturdy one, and everything she'd left back on the shore was becoming small and fuzzy, then no longer discernible, falling away below the curve of the earth.

CEDRIC S. MESMER

He's taking in the air again with
the insight of a basement plant.
I can't look into those long eyes long
enough to travel the gulf, or
to light a purple and blue-edged fire
on the beach.
If he'll look, our favored poet
of the sweet-to-sickening, dull lit den, Look
through the aquarium, each side a lens,
He will see the beach with freshly charred shores, and a
harbor deeper than his eye.

A purple iris blooms in that night, like the opening of the eyes of a freshly born prophet,
it has blue markings to seal the night
at its edges
into wax.
I am here, rubbing paper sticks and pounding flint,
with a glint of indigo under my lashes,
spreading leaves of laurels from the ash
at my knees, running up, pouring over
my left shoulder.
There is a maze of loosestrife light
pouring forth from my veins inside my head.

ADAM HENRY CARRIERE

Postcard

roses, wine, and october are red
violets, the moon, and meanies are blue
sugar, sex, and heroin is sweet
i'm in europe going mad . . . without you

The Good Baron

Join the good Baron's race

what delight he brings the children
all of us

on a dark, moonbeam-swept eve

tone poems
civil, grand, and elegant
a masque for our wintered souls

life as an operetta

He will smile and all will be well

our fantasies become unbound

Vienna, forever
Radetsky, god
the empire, the world

Death itself will be cheated

a grand ricochet through a time of dreams
and the incorruptible happiness

white uniforms, blue blood
gold piping, red cannonfire

that becomes ours

polka française

escape

KURT SMITH

Scrambled Eggs

Walt's admiring his plate—a steaming ham and cheese omelette, chunks of tomato and green pepper poking out, hash browns cooked dark.

"Hey, Willy, hand me that saltshaker there, will ya'."

Willy passes the salt to Walt, who douses his food liberally.

"Thanks," says Walt. Willy nods.

Delmer, spreading raspberry jam on his toast, says to Walt, "You'll never get a job with J. C. Penney the way you shake on the salt like that. You're supposed to at least taste it first."

"I know what it tastes like. I eat here every morning. So do you. The eggs always need salt."

Merle's opening a plastic creamer for his coffee. "I hate these things. Guy could poke his finger right through these skimpy lids tryin' to get 'em off."

"Yeah, I know what you mean. I've done it," says Walt.

"So what'ya been up to, Del?" asks Willy as he lifts one of his hotcakes with a fork and pours maple syrup on the one underneath.

"Not much. Sylvia and I watched that new show on TV last night. That new cop show with a guy that wears the eye patch. Can't think of his name? You know the one I mean . . . guy gets outta' prison and becomes a private investigator . . . wears an eye patch. What's his name?"

Merle, speaking through a mouthful of waffle, asks, "Is he the one who was in that movie with . . . oh . . . that good-looking dame with the tattoo on her shoulder that my wife doesn't like me lookin' at? You know who I mean, the one that was married, to, eh, can't think of his name . . ."

"I know who you mean," says Willy, cutting up one of his hotcakes into neat small squares. "Won the Academy Award last year for best actor."

"No he didn't," says Walt, pulling out a piece of green pepper. "Just nominated. Didn't win."

"Oh yes, he won," says Delmer, dipping his toast point into the runny part of his egg. "I'm pretty sure he won. If he didn't win, who did?"

"He didn't win because what's-his-face won," answers Merle, spreading marmalade across one section of his waffle.

"What's-his-face? Who's what's-his-face?" asks Willy.

"The same guy who was in that movie about the serial

killer who tried to blow up the stadium at the World Series between the Reds and . . . some other team?"

"What year was it?" asks Walt, who's now shaking pepper onto his omelette.

"Well, it wasn't any particular year," answers Willy. "It was just in the movie, but it showed some of the real players from the two teams."

Willy slurps more coffee just as Doreen, who carries a pencil behind her ear, comes by with the carafe.

Delmer asks, "Doreen, you see a lot of movies. Who won the Academy Award for best actor last year?"

"Two years ago," says Walt, slicing a tomato chunk with his fork handle.

"Well, which is it? Last year or two years ago?" Doreen asks as she hands Walt a knife from her apron pocket.

"Last year."

"I don't know," she says, leaning over to pour coffee into Willy's cup.

"Two years ago," says Walt.

"Al Pacino?" she offers.

"No, that was three years ago," says Willy. *"Smell of a Woman."*

"Scent of a Woman," corrects Doreen.

"Scent, smell. What's the difference?"

"A lot," Doreen snuffs. Walt and Del laugh out loud.

"I thought what's-his-name won best actor that year," says Merle. "You know who I mean. Rowdy Yates."

"Clint Eastwood," fills in Walt.

"Yeah. Clint Eastwood. What was the name of that movie?" asks Delmer, adding another spoonful of jam to his toast.

"I think the Eastwood movie won," says Willy, "but

Pacino won the acting award. I think the movie was what won it for Clint."

"*Unforgiven*," says Doreen.

"Yep. That's it," says Willy. "So who won this year?"

"Oh, I know," says Doreen, "it was that guy in . . . the one about the gangsters who talk about cheeseburgers and all that . . . and that girl with the black hair . . . what's her name?"

"You mean that tall one with long legs and she was in that one show where she was the girlfriend, I think, of, oh, what's his name . . . the guy who's been in a lot of really good movies . . . big star . . . can't think of his name," says Delmer.

"You know," says Merle, who licks a marmalade drip off the side of his fork, "they make the best cheeseburgers at that new little place over on Fourteenth. Lots of french fries."

"Oh, yeah, I heard of that place. Owned by one of the Olson boys, right?" observes Willy.

"Yep. I believe you're right. Let's see, there's three of them. The oldest is the one that had that little Chevy truck that was all fixed up . . . what was his name?"

"Was it Earl?" asks Walt.

"Earl doesn't sound right," says Willy. "Maybe Bart? Tony? I can't remember. Anyway, the next one was Jim."

"Nope, the next one was Bob," says Delmer. "So Jim musta been the youngest one. Bob's the one married that Spencer girl. What was her name? Redheaded girl. Had a brother named . . . oh, what was his name . . . played quarterback on that team we had here that went to the playoffs. That girl's brother, the redheaded girl . . . her brother was the quarterback on that team. What year was that, you remember?"

"It musta been after 1971," says Walt, whose omelette is now smeared with catsup.

"It was the same year they took that old building down over there on Flint Street," says Merle. "Belonged to the . . . eh, what was the name of that family owned that store? Furniture and appliances. You remember what I'm talking about, Willy?"

"Yeah, I think the old man bought that place from anther guy, back in the late fifties, let's see . . . had been a car dealership there, and he sold it to . . . I can't think of the name of the guy who bought it . . . but he sold furniture there and then he sold it to another small outfit. . . ."

"No," says Walt, "you're thinking of that place that sold tires and then they sold that place to a young fella' who came in and made it into a wholesale store for car parts and that kind of stuff. Had some name like Nifty Auto Supply, or Happy Auto Supply. Remember?"

Doreen is wiping off the catsup bottle.

"Doreen, what was the name of that auto parts store over on, let's see, about Fourteenth or Fifteenth Avenue? Went out of business back in, oh, probably about six, seven years ago?"

"It was more like ten years ago," says Merle, who's squinting to read the small print on the back of the Tabasco bottle.

"I don't remember," says Doreen. "Maybe something like Roscoe's Tires?"

"No, Roscoe's Tires was over on Grant. That place burned down . . . no, this was a parts store . . . Nifty Parts, something like that. You remember, Willy?"

"Was it next to that place that sold sheet metal?"

"Sheet metal? I don't remember a sheet metal place. Where are you talking about?"

"That place over by the dike."

"By the water tower?" asks Delmer, stirring his eggs with the last piece of his toast.

"No, over more by the bridge. Closer to the bridge."

"Oh, you mean by the old Shepard place?" asks Willy.

"Closer this way than there," says Walt, dragging a fork of hash browns through the catsup.

"Old man Shepard. You hear about them?" asks Willy.

"No, what'd you hear?" Merle's sluicing a syrup channel across his plate with his final waffle section.

Willy puts his hand atop his coffee cup when Doreen offers another fill-up. "Wife up and walked out on him. Just like that."

"No kidding. She just left, eh? Got tired of his ways, I guess," muses Delmer.

"Now she was one of the Newton girls, right?" asks Walt, winding a string of melted cheese around his fork.

"Yeah," says Delmer. "Had a couple sisters. Let's see, I think one of them was named . . . eh, let's see, maybe LuAnne. Linda. Willy, you remember that family? What were their names, anyway?"

"Yeah, I'll think of it in a second. The oldest one was married to the guy who sold televisions. What was his name?"

"Waring."

Delmer glugs the rest of his coffee. "Yeah, I think that was it. I think Waring is right. His brother drove ambulance and was on the city council for a couple of years. Ran for mayor. What was his name?"

Doreen places the bill on the table, which Willy shoves toward Merle.

"Oh, let's see," answers Walt, scooping the last of his hash browns onto his fork with his knife, "I think his name might have been Harold. Wasn't he the one who won free tickets to some big football game one year?"

"Yeah, Super Bowl tickets. Won some drawing and got Super Bowl tickets. What Super Bowl was that, anyway? Willy, you remember what one that was? I believe he went to Miami, but he had to pay his own airfare, but he went anyway. You remember that, Willy?"

"I don't remember what Super Bowl it was, but I think he might have gone to Dallas. Did they have a Super Bowl in Dallas? Or was it in Houston?"

"New Orleans had it one year," says Delmer. "I remember watching that one on TV"

"Hey, that was some game, eh?"

"Yeah," says Merle. "Boy, that new TV that Barbara's brother and his wife got is sure a beauty. Big old screen. A guy could see it from here if the bank wasn't in the way. Got big speakers. You know how that Dolby sound in the theater has that wraparound sound? This dang TV has that, too. You stand anywhere in the house you can see and hear it."

"So, Walt, you been watching any those new shows?" Delmer asks.

"Oh, yeah. But I was still watch mostly the news and sports. Once in a while I watch the late shows or some movie."

"Me, too. Mostly sports. I still like *Jeopardy,*" says Willy.

"Yeah, I like it too," says Walt. "Oh, and there's that new show on last night. That cop show with some guy wearing an eye patch. Can't think of his name."

"I saw it, too," Willy says, stirring the last bite of hotcake around his plate with his fork.

"Yeah, so did I," says Merle, as he stuffs the little plastic creamer containers on top of each other and squinches them into a compact shape.

Delmer squints to read the bill, then puts his money on the pile with the rest. "Well, boys, I think I'm going to go mow my lawn. See you tomorrow."

"Yeah, I got some work to do, too," says Willy, pulling on his windbreaker.

Walt puts the saltshaker back in its place by the napkin holder and carefully lays his fork on the shiny omelette plate. "Yep, might as well get started. See you boys tomorrow."

JENNIFER VELASCO

It's Time I Wasn't Here

We sped through tunnel visions
of green signs, billboards
and rubber sheared from tires
that looks like road kill.
Amy and Greg sit in a formaldehyde silence
as I drive us to Columbia
to see Uncle Tupelo at The Blue Note.

We blend in with the crowd
that slams beer and sweat against us,
and while Amy and Greg stand on opposite sides,

glaring at each other over their drinks,
I try to dance in the cigarette haze
but only stagger along
and keep drinking.

When it ends
and we come back down for home
they explode like cats on their way to the vet
as fast and as loud as the band played.
I just turn the stereo up
though my ears and head are still buzzing.
We didn't get that far.

But I'll take the next chance I can
to leave this town—and them—behind,
leave to get lost,
find the way back though not out,
and tell everyone I've been somewhere.

MICHELLE RIEMAN

---

rue de mort et amitié

moon smile shimmers down the soft and slick cold tin
multicolored friandise block life's bitter touch again
but can not pass through blood and flesh to sweet his
heart within

the satellite affection pulls his mouth and groin and bone
he gains the silver beacon which kiss-whispers him come
        home

a faintest wind abets, the palms applaud his bend
he swallows laughs then slips
from the roof into the fen

MATHEW SANBORN SMITH

Better than Anything

That damn tapping woke him up, echoing from somewhere downstairs, beneath the heart of the house. Greg swallowed to soothe his dry throat and pressed the clock stud in the headboard. Excited dust motes, once carefree in their nowhere drift, clung to each other in a passionate frenzy in the clock's field. *12:07 P.M.*, they glowed for an instant before burning to nothingness while he heard the time whispered in the windless bedroom.

Kelly was gone. About an hour and twenty-seven minutes, he judged, running the coolness of the sheets through the ultrasensitive fingers of the Glove. They'd made love last night (the Glove still smelled it on the sheets), just like Greg had fantasized when they were in high school together. Well, not exactly like he'd fantasized; he wasn't the same person he'd been in high school.

He studied the creases in his skin at the bathroom mirror, fascinated by what his wrinkled bedding had left for him to read. He fancied himself a scarified tribal chief while running his one bare hand under icy water. Finally he fell flaccid so he could piss before his bladder burst. Nothing had been in to clean for a while. Not much of a need since he'd never had a woman stay the entire night before. Nights with a lady usually brought screams and a quick scramble to throw her scattered clothes into the crook of one arm and she was gone, past the limo driver who had learned to wait for the familiar scenario. The women, more often than not, felt like they had escaped rather than left. He never chased them; he understood. He just wished they would understand that he got more out of lovemaking through the Glove's eleven senses than he could ever get from his penis's one. The Glove gave more to his partner, too. Kelly had reveled in it and because of that, he enjoyed it even more than usual. It was the first decent night he'd had since the new season's push had gotten under way. His belly burned just remembering the job.

Reynolds OmniMedia needed a ratings-phenomenon for the Reports, that much was obvious. With the legalization of Obsession, business had been ass-over-elbows downhill and picking up speed at ten Gs a second. But the holy Alliance had ordered a spring purge and cleansing of the flesh this month. There would be no better time to get people onmind once again before ROM and its kind became long forgotten memory among powerstims. And Greg Herod felt like he was dancing on air . . . with the ground rushing up to meet him at a thousand feet per second.

Downstairs, Kelly Bourne bounced her wide bottom

lightly on her chair, tapping on Greg's 19thCen dining table with a polished teaspoon. A red stim dangled lazily from beneath her tongue. *Guess drool doesn't bother her much,* Greg thought. He had just come down, naked from the bedroom, dragging his feet along the rich cream carpet, beckoned by her *tap-tap-tap*. She was a beautiful woman, and her large frame only emphasized it. The maroon and gold of her painted nails contrasted exquisitely with her blond hair and the white silk pajamas she seemed to have pulled out of nowhere. She was a vision and Greg wondered for a moment if he couldn't have her here every morning lighting up his palace with her elegant splendor. *Marriage? Jesus, last night wasn't that good, was it?* He snuck up behind her and swept the spoon from her loose grasp with his incongruous left hand, black and ridged from fingertips to three-quarters of the way up his forearm. It was the Glove, permanently attached and the ticket to the good life that he lived right now.

"Oh," she said, "You scared me." Her plastic stim tinkled to the table and she wiped her mouth on a cloth napkin. "What's wrong, real silver?"

"Yes, but more importantly, the table is real wood." He pulled a chair from the wall and pulled up next to her.

"I'm sorry, I didn't know."

She was even more beautiful than she had been in high school, or maybe it was just that the peer pressure was off now. Back then her enormous size had marked her as a girl not to be dated for fear of recrimination from the other jocks. They all said she was fat. She wasn't though. She was just large. Her size intimidated most guys. Kelly and Greg had been friends and Greg had always thought about going with her but never seemed to get around to asking. But last night after nine years of adulthood and real world, not to mention a towering confidence that didn't exist before the Glove, he'd just about climbed onto her lap at the United Media dinner to the paparazzi's delight.

She was an executive with Reynolds East, the advertising end of the game. He'd forgotten her father had swung in the upper echelons of the company years ago, her obvious inroad. When he bumped into her at the UM for the first time since high school, everything had fallen into place.

"I was waiting for you," she said now. "I guess I was getting bored."

"Bored? You should have turned on the Reports."

"Oh, no. They don't really do a whole lot for me. I've got to live them, practically."

"I do live them," he said, smiling.

"That's right, I forgot for a second. How long have you had this thing?" she asked, caressing the Glove like a cow's udder.

"About five years now. Dar had it for nine and Germane for thirteen, so I figure I still have some time left."

"You think they're going to give you a few more years to live and hand the Glove to the next young kid?"

"I don't see why they shouldn't. The Glove is the star of the show. I'm basically just a pretty face to carry it around and smile for the Reports. I'll probably think of some way out of it by that time."

"Its last two owners didn't." She had a bowl of oatmeal in front of her, still steaming slightly. She started to eat, not shaken by the Glove at all, but maybe her line of work had just made her jaded. And maybe that's why those awful thoughts of marriage were creeping into his head now.

His link buzzed.

Greg nodded and took it on personal. "Yeah?"

"This is it, you ready?" It was his controller, Sharky.

Sharky knew the business backward and throughout and Greg took pains to stay on his best side. When the shit came down six years from now, nobody was going to be able to help Greg more. This call was the one Greg hadn't wanted to take. ROM was lighting the fuse. He was their biggest star by far, the only Action Celebrity that wasn't completely created by Reynolds, the only one who had abilities beyond that of human technology. So when they wanted digits, it was Greg that got tossed into the inferno. And as the consumer took it all more and more for granted, Reynolds played him on bigger and bigger risks. No matter what he told Kelly, he was sure this week, the biggest blitz on the public staged yet, would be the week that killed him.

"It's a bomb, down in the 'burbs right by you. A plasma bomb," Sharky whined.

"Holy shit. Why didn't they get Blacksmith to do it? That's his bag."

"He'll be there too, but their excuse for having you along is that his hands haven't grown back yet. Just be glad your crisis has arrived and you don't have to worry about it anymore."

"Oh, no, there's nothing to worry about now. Wheeeee!"

"Get on the shuttle in seventeen minutes. Don't be late or else there won't be any place to go to anyway." He clicked off.

"Gotta go," Greg said. "Martin can let you out."

"What is it?" She suddenly seemed anxious.

"Just biz."

"What kind of biz? Stay here and let the next guy handle it."

"Look, I know my job better than you do. I gotta hurry, it's an emergency."

"Wait!"

"What?"

"You remember what we talked about last night?"

"Only vaguely. My left hemisphere dissolved in the champagne around one-thirty."

"We talked about early retirement, Greggy, remember? Quit it now, right now, before you go out and they kill you."

"I can't. Not now. It's an emergency!"

"They're making it an emergency, can't you see that? Let someone else do it and you're a normal person again, with your own life. You've got enough money now to do whatever you want."

He wasn't listening, just struggling into a torn-up pair of jeans he liked to call his Robinson Crusoes.

"Do you think for yourself anymore, Greg? Why don't you lose that glove for God's sake? Ask it to leave?"

"Look, you don't understand how it is. Things have changed since the last time you saw me."

"What things?"

"Don't you remember me eight years ago? I was studying full throttle just to get Ds, I got fired from five jobs senior year alone, and I was sleeping in my truck because my parents threw me out of the house. I was a nobody. I was worse than a nobody, I was a loser. And it didn't end there. I'd be dead already if it wasn't for the Glove, from alcohol maybe or a gunshot to the head. This is the only thing that makes me anybody. It's the only thing I'm good at! Ask anybody."

"It's not true," she whispered, shaking her head. "You're obsessed with that thing, it's taking over your personality."

"You didn't seem to mind it last night."

Her eyes grew cold, and she went back to eating her oatmeal. Somehow he knew she wasn't talking to him any longer. It's not like he could tell her anyway.

"What's this all about anyway?" he asked, "Did Reynolds send you here?"

Kelly let her spoon sink to the bottom of the bowl and rose swiftly. She slapped him hard enough to almost knock him over. "I have to go." She walked away without sparing him a glance and went to the bedroom. Either she was sent by Reynolds and was a good actress or she actually liked him. It was hard to believe this second one.

"Just go home to Chicago!" he yelled, wondering why the evacuation hadn't yet begun. "Fast as you can!"

He tried to get in touch with Sharky on the shuttle. No answer. Sharky had smelled death and bolted. "Thanks a lot for your confidence, asshole," Greg muttered. He passed the short trip watching the last-minute evacuation on the Reports. Muted anxiety squeezed a small neighborhood with artiturf lawns and fiberglass watchdogs. The National Guard loaded trucks with people who didn't want to stay but didn't necessarily want to go either. One man tried to bring his wide-screen monitor into one of the mottled gray trucks only to have it thrown to the ground and smashed when he refused to give it up. Its shattered plaz was the closest thing to a cry for help the addled neighborhood could muster. Greg ate a spotted banana while he watched a scene recorded earlier of the Bartons, the people unfortunate enough to rent the property on which the bomb had been found. Mr. Barton, still in a worn red plaid robe with a fringe of threads hanging from the bottom, held the poodle that had uncovered the device. His wife, squinting without her glasses, stared down the viewer while crying that they had no place to stay, that their son was fighting in the war, and that her sister had disappeared when they tried to reach her. The reporter asked them if they had any enemies. Greg roared with laughter. "What the hell could these people have done that would make someone plant a plasma bomb with a fifty-kilometer radius on their land?" he shouted at the Report. The reporter's question was ludicrous and yet he asked in the hope that other numbers would think that it could happen to them too.

Then the sensors panned across the yard to show a bomb squad making final preps with the Blacksmith before fleeing into a white chopper. Greg felt his stomach flip-flop more from the sight of him than the fact that he'd hardly eaten. He had hoped the Big Stim would be a one-man show, or least that he'd be teamed with someone other than the Blacksmith. The Blacksmith was the unofficial leader of the Ac-Cels who hated Greg Herod either for his power, his fame, or a little of both. Aside from that, the guy was an asshole to the *n*th degree. Too bad plasma bombs were his business.

Everybody and his uncle had a plasma bomb these days; practically the fashion. A hell of a lot easier to make than a standard hydrogen bomb because the parts weren't illegal to buy, own, or ship. Sure, it was more expensive than an office building in Bhopal, but it was feasible. The gate could be bought by a government, and its registration laundered, and as long as you had a power source big enough you were in business.

The air near the Barton residence (possibly the former Barton residence) was thick with microscopic stim sensors. Reynolds had the area under an army of security bots to keep the competition out for at least a half hour. More than enough time for the bomb to go off.

Greg felt the sensors salivating as they gobbled up his presence. He was an institution, a one-man SWAT force known as the Fist on the Reports. Not quite as flashy as the young sucks calling themselves Action Celebrities nowadays, but he didn't need flash. He had substance. He had prime numbers, with a history that went back to the last generation.

He'd changed into his costume just before walking out. It made him feel more of a freak than usual, focusing attention on the Glove, what the Reports liked to call the Anything Glove, because that was what it was capable of. The Glove had a name before its wearer did. His entire outfit was deep red save for the Glove. He thanked God he didn't have to wear a mask; his looks saved his identity. Unlike Beowulf or Odd, he was a person, not a costume. A person who carried this thing at the end of his arm.

"Take a seat, hotshot," the Blacksmith called to him. Greg took it without a word. His life depended on this man and he wasn't about to start a fight. There was a small pit around the bomb, allowing as much access to it as possible without moving the thing. On the edge of the pit, like the king of the cockroaches with the dirt as his throne, sat the Blacksmith, real name: Ronnie Moscowitz, the man so famous for defusing bombs he nearly had three-quarters of the Fist's numbers. "There isn't anything the Blacksmith can't defuse," they say. Except maybe his appetite, Greg thought. Three hundred and two pounds, his Glove remembered for him. And the man was short on top of that. Sure, someone standing six-ten, six-eleven might wear three hundred pounds pretty well, might even be considered slim, but at five-eight the Blacksmith looked like a pig.

But he was the best. Tore up that warhead the Ibn

Mahesh boys got a hold of. Took it apart with the world standing over his shoulder, right in the middle of Washington Colum. Gained lasting fame when he rode the KItel-Sat as it burned through the sky and he snuffed the self-destruct when it threatened to come right down on the head of Beijing's financial district and wiped out three city blocks. He saved countless lives and thousands of acres of priceless property and was considered a national hero. But now he sat in a pile of dirt while Greg had a 50K plasma bomb between his legs. At the end of the Blacksmith's arms were two white regen tubes ending in temporary plaz fingers that were useless for this type of job. The tubes covered the stumps that were his hands three weeks ago, before they were blown off as he idly tossed a hand grenade to himself. Greg had smirked when he heard the news. Now he wondered how much bad karma a simple smirk was worth, because today the Blacksmith wanted the Fist to be his hands.

Staring at the bomb, Greg couldn't think about the town and city it was about to destroy or about the tens of thousands of people it was about to kill. The only thing that he could imagine was how it was going to feel to be blown away one-tenth of a second after detonation by a minute chunk of that sun that was beating down on them, transported eight light-minutes in an instant by the gate with the laundered registration.

He felt the bomb's electronic heartbeat through the Glove, a hum that seemed deafening, though it was a whisper compared to the harsh pulsing of the blood through his veins. It was all too real, too alive, slowly coiling to a precise tension that would unleash itself in all God's fury in just seven minutes and he hoped they could stop it. His mouth filled with spit, like it always did just before he threw up, because he remembered that *he* was "they" and it was up to him to stop it and he didn't know what the hell he was doing.

It was the Glove's fault. The power at the end of his left arm that made him the most widely recognized person in the world, according to Gallup. Discovered by an international exploration team off of Barnard's Star twenty-seven years ago, it was the first-known piece of extraterrestrial space garbage. It was a piece of trash, a McDonald's wrapper tossed by some alien out the car window as it zoomed through a no-name galaxy. A piece of trash that made Earth call back its little ships and adjust its focus to hiding from the universe it once believed it could conquer. The thing had looked like a living Koosh ball made of crude oil when they first brought it on board the research vessel *Brahe*. After a few days it decided against spending any more time in their labs and escaped to make contact with Robin Dar, an astrophysicist who changed professions soon after her return to Earth. It became a glove when it met her, *the* Glove, and hasn't made any long-lasting changes since. Reynolds had snapped up Dar with a fat contract the minute her slender foot had hit civilian ground and ushered in the era of the Action Celebrity. And now, a generation later, Greg Herod looked at the thing that made him one of the richest stars in the world and despised it. *We might all be killed, but you'll survive and crawl onto the next person in line,* he thought.

The Blacksmith puffed on his cigar, cool as a killer's knife. He always got that way around bombs, the only time he really relaxed. After a long, slow drag, he rationed his speaking breath like a miser. "Not sure why they called me in at all. Pretty whiz kid like you oughta be able to handle the whole operation with that supercrutch your career's leaning on."

"You want to leave?" Greg asked. "Why don't you run down that chopper?"

The Blacksmith let cigar smoke twist from between his yellow, solid teeth. His look said he was ready to pounce if he could, but he just said, "Get your boy through that screen, first off. There's a few different detonators in these things. You try and take off that screen, you'll trigger one of 'em."

Greg's fingers grew as long and as thin as knitting needles and the Glove penetrated the mesh screen which separated him from the internal workings of the bomb.

Moscowitz sat back and spoke with the air of a backwater lecturer leaning against a pickle barrel. "You'll see they use different bombs and situations to hook different numbers. Most of 'em ain't this elaborate. Usually, for an investigative angle, the bomb could be gasoline and a nine volt, they'll just hide the damn thing and the whole show'll be on finding it. On those, I'm suddenly the big criminal psychologist, who tracks it down 'cuz he knows how these terrorists think.

"Ones like the KItel-Sat are just plain old action, like I'm fuckin' James Bond or something." He choked out a loud laugh, spitting his cigar into the freshly turned earth. "These ones here are for numbers who're into MacGyver."

"What the hell is MacGyver?"

"Forget it. The numbers don't remember either, but they eat it up. I like to think of 'em as puzzle bombs."

"I don't give a damn what you think of them," Greg said, "just as long as you keep your torn-up ass on the business at hand and let me live after six minutes from now." Moscowitz chuckled, like he had something on him.

"There's a seal here," Greg told him. "It's a . . ." He didn't want to believe it. Saying it out loud would make it true and he didn't want it to be true.

"It's a what?" the fat man yelled.

"It's an atomic lock."

"Oh, Christ," the Blacksmith whispered. He touched his throat mike with his right stub and relayed this to his superiors. He nodded slowly as his inner ear received the instructions Greg couldn't hear, and said:

"It's a safe bet whoever designed this thing doesn't want to let us in. So the key is gonna be something very rare and possibly unstable. Now, unless you have something in that hand that can figure out what we need and transport it here immediately, we're fucked. Plan B is to pick your favorite direction and run like your ass is on fire."

Greg fought dizziness now, trying desperately to keep a grip on the rational, thinking part of his brain because he knew that no matter what else it could do, the Glove couldn't get him away far enough, fast enough to escape.

"Wait," he said. "My glove. It changes shape. I can try to pour myself into the lock till it's the shape of the key, fill the lock, and open it."

"That's great," he said, "but we don't know what the hell kind of atom it'll be until the exact microsecond you become it. It could fall apart and fry the shit out of us."

"Would you rather die now maybe, or die in five minutes definitely?" Greg watched the sweat dribbling out from between the thick ripples of fat on his partner's neck. The Report's instant editors never showed that to the public. What else were they editing now?

"Do it, already!"

He did it and he could feel subatomic particles snapping into their tiny orbits. His heart beat twice for every electron/proton pair that he added to the formula and still his work was rapid. He found himself slowing as he neared the minefield toward the end of the periodic table. Suddenly, his wrist expanded into an impenetrable black dome which surrounded the bomb. Looking up, he felt a shiver at the bottom of his back. The Blacksmith saw Greg's look of surprise at what happened and he looked like he found out something dirty, some vile secret about the Fist.

"It sometimes acts to protect its owner without my instructions," Greg explained with a sheepish smile. The Blacksmith leaned back, slowly, now regarding the Glove as an unpredictable animal, rather than a product of an unknown science.

Something was wrong.

"I'm stuck," Greg said.

"What do you mean, *stuck?*" His eyes darted around the obsidian shield of the Glove, vainly attempting to see through to the problem.

"I've got ninety-four electrons and as many protons in place. The lock's full up but it's not opening."

With a soft thud, the Blacksmith nearly damaged himself as his right stump darted to his throat mike. He spoke quickly, but remained coherent.

"Isotopes!" he shrieked.

Greg's breath returned to him as the Glove now continued its work. Why didn't *it* take care of that in the first place?

"There it is!" he cried, feeling the lock open. "It's plutonium 244. Stable enough, though it was dicey getting to it. The shield wants to stay in place," he added, almost as an aside. "I can feel my way through from here." Two minutes and counting.

The Blacksmith asked him, "What's next?"

Even with the glow of the inner clock, the light within the bomb was virtually nonexistent. But although the Glove is capable of more senses than an unaided human, its sense of touch has always been its most superior sense and Greg trusted it through the remainder of this operation.

"There are some buttons." He felt the painted marks to identify their function. "They're . . ."

"What? They're what?" the Blacksmith yelled.

"It's a transport gate," he said, not quite believing himself. "Not the plasma transporter, it's the kind with the buttons. It's a second gate."

The Blacksmith's eyes grew wide. "What?" He was on his throat mike again. "Oh shit! It's not supposed to be there!"

"What do you mean? What do I do, you fat son of a bitch? Hurry!"

"I don't know, I wasn't briefed on this!" His voice was wet and cracking. He was about to get up (to do what? run?) when Greg willed forth from the Glove a metallic leash around the Blacksmith's throat to quiet him, and he looked into the Blacksmith's eyes.

"You aren't shit, are you? All the shit you've given me about being nothing without the Glove and now the truth comes out. All this time I thought you knew your stuff and you were just an actor. Well, don't worry about the bomb, because I'm killing you before it blows!"

"Nggg!" the Blacksmith said as he pointed to his head. Greg released him as a soft female synthetic voice said over the Blacksmith's amplifiers:

"This is the Reynolds OmniMedia emergency crisis containment unit. Please enter the following jumpgate coordinates: Del. Del. Sig. Pi. Omi. Del. Omi."

"No!" Greg yelled. "It's a setup!"

"What? You crazy son of a bitch, punch it in!"

"But anything could . . ." A cold realization settled to the bottom of Greg's stomach. "You people didn't need me to crack this bomb. You wanted me to take on whatever's coming through this gate, whether its an army or a nanocloud!"

"Look, we needed you for both. We can argue about this later. If there is any later in twenty-seven seconds, god-damit!" He looked at his chronometer and desperately whacked his stump against the Glove's improvised dome, cracking his regen tube. Green liquid spilled out, exposing an embryonic set of fingers.

Greg willed the leash around the fat man's throat once again. "Listen, you bastard, this glove gives me the power to wipe out anything Reynolds can throw at me. You know I can crush whatever's coming through the gate and you should also know I'm crushing you next. And Reynolds is in deeper shit than you, because contact or not, I'm taking control from here on out." Greg took satisfaction in the slight bulge of the Blacksmith's eyes as the Glove punched in the code Greg had already forgotten in the heat of the moment. The clock ticked off its last three seconds and Greg prayed to God that he wasn't about to be blown to hell.

He screamed when the burst of heat and light from the gate that appeared at his side burned his skin. He screamed more from fear than pain, imagining for a second that the bomb was exploding. The Glove tugged at his hand, like it wanted to separate itself from him. Almost instantly Greg collected himself and turned to face the foe from the gate.

Ronnie Moscowitz, born loser, thrust into fame by a fluke, laughed triumphantly, forgotten by the Glove's leash. "Reynolds can't wait another six years, Pretty Boy. The funny thing is, without your five-fingered money machine, they couldn't have afforded their little jaunt to Barnard's Star."

Greg's gut was ice and his eyes were trained on the large woman before him. She wore a suit made of a black, ridged material. It covered her from scalp to sole with one notable exception: Her left hand was bare, its nails painted maroon and gold.

ALAN WALKER

Frankie's Resting

Frank is resting in his bed,
nestled covers round his head.
Have his thoughts now turned to lead
and flowed molten through the ears?

Frank is resting in bed.
How he hates me (so he said).
Has he forgiven me instead,
or am I in his thoughts at all?

Frank is resting in his bed.
Should I go and hold his head,
or throw water on his head?
I doubt if this would help things.

Miss Sweden

So now we come to Sweden
The cold Northland of Bergman
The cold Northland of handsome
men, sometimes gone bad.
Have you had, did you have.
She has. She is not a man.
You shouldn't blame her if
she works for the Paternal Association,
negotiating many of the secret
artistic abilities that make her her.
You shouldn't blame her if she
wears blue.
Blue can be forgiven.

JUDY RYAN

Straw Creek Wilderness

I never would have known about Straw Creek if it hadn't been for an epic excess of Nature. When the Flood of '93 inundated Iowa, I was forced to find high ground for my walks outdoors. The creekside nature trails where my dog and I normally walked were under six feet of water, and even well-developed forest pathways were impassable that year.

I had heard about a county park that I thought was worth investigating. Straw Creek Park is only fifteen minutes from where I live, and because one must drive through the countryside to get there, it seems to be farther away from the city than it really is. I was getting desperate for somewhere to walk in relative solitude, and I was delighted to discover a paved roadway that loops through forest, prairie, grassland, and wetland in a compact, two-mile circle. It climbs a hill that is steep enough to provide beneficial exercise, and it leads to a far-reaching panoramic view at the top.

I had found a way to continue my nature hikes come hell or high water.

The first indication that there was something special about Straw Creek Park arrived with dusk when I first walked the circle at sundown. It was like stepping into Kevin Costner's rural heaven at the conclusion of *Field of Dreams*. "People will come." A long line of slow-moving cars, with headlights on low beam, crept between the base of a wooded hill on one side and an expanse of grassy meadow on the other. People do come, to see the deer. They are never disappointed.

Every evening as the sun goes down the whitetails emerge from the forest to step gently through the tall grass along a network of well-worn game trails. With heads held high, they carefully cross the road. Spotted fawns follow watchful does. Bucks step proudly from the trees, their antlers parting low-slung branches like theater curtains.

It's a ritual honored by the same creatures night after night, and I became one of them. I learned to love Straw

Creek Park simply, subtly, and, although I didn't recognize it immediately, spiritually.

The flooding that sent me in search of dry ground receded into memory, but I continued to walk at Straw Creek, abandoning my former haunts completely. I have never known a place that offers so many different landscapes so sweetly and succinctly.

The park's access road is lined by restored prairie. It leads to a parking lot and lodge at the base of a hill that in winter is strewn with sleds and toboggans. From there the road rises gently but steadily between tree-covered hillsides. It curves to the left at the feet of massive oak sentinels that guard the mowed clearings where picnic tables stand. The oaks dominate the hilltop, and walking beneath them is like traveling back through time to seek the wisdom that ancient sages and prophets must surely have entrusted to such enduring messengers.

Congenial curves guide the walker from under the shelter of the massive branches to an exposed clearing at the very top of the hill. Straight ahead, above and beyond the crowns of lesser and lower trees, lie acres of cultivated fields bordered by hazy treelines of other ridges and rises. Below to the left are the grassy meadows where the deer graze at sunset. To the right a dense woodland drops steeply, its vegetation broken only where narrow game trails pierce the darkness.

A steep descent, slippery with loose gravel, curves left again until the walker is at the base of the hill where prairie grasses bend toward cottonwoods and river birches on the banks of an unseen creek. The trees speak of water as their leaves rustle in even the gentlest of breezes.

The road comes full circle; the lodge lies ahead. In the heat and humidity the grasses grow taller than the tallest deer, but black-eyed Susans and Queen Anne's lace, the undaunted ladies of summer, still thrive along the roadside.

In autumn the forest floor reappears, shimmering with golden leaves tossed noisily aside by chipmunks and squirrels scurrying from fallen log to fallen limb.

In winter the road is closed to traffic and the peace is overwhelming.

Carpets of delicate lavender blossoms spread out at the feet of each approaching spring when new life stirs at Straw Creek Park.

My dog and I walked though three full seasonal cycles. Three years of continuous discovery in a place almost mystical in its timelessness. Where nature is a life force that draws the unsuspecting admirer into an energizing intimacy. Where you have to return again and again, lured by sunlight and soft breezes, by gray skies and snow shadows, by the call of something too primitive to name, too essential to ignore.

We walked for three years in such promising peacefulness, my dog and I. Then the road builders came.

E. A. GIBSON

Hunter

Stealth is in the way he climbs a tree:
slowly, his hands and feet bearing the weight of his body,
his fingers gripping the bark,
wrapping around the limbs, pulling.

Braced, he's the landscape:
pale inside winter's bright chill,
cool under the distant hum of a waking sun,
quiet, like the snow falling,
waiting.

His bow is the tender brown of frozen earth,
a branch among branches.
Its string pulled tight,
like the muscles in his arms when he poises the arrow,
the roses of his breath floating like birds on the morning air.

The arrow, when it flies,
cuts the air with a hush
and meets the deer's heart with a stunning thud.
Her long legs buckle one joint at a time,
her life soon closed in the bright morning light,
his renewed by the artfulness of the chase,
its triumphant end.

CLIFF BOYER

Entering Calaway County

(At the time of the Mississippi Flood, Summer '93)

The huge land whale
lumbered along
the straight gray channel
while four-wheeled pilot fish
clustered around her,
wiggling into position.

On the flooded shore floated
the Mark Twain Bank
and Noah's Ark Motor Inn.

amlet: "Alas, poor Yorick!" KOURTNEY HARPER

TERESA HAMANN

Chutes and Ladders

I surprised my friends when I broke off the relationship. Angie, lovable but blunt, got right down to it and said, "Glory, it would be a whole lot easier to believe that *he* dumped *you*. I can't understand it. The man has everything. What were you thinking?" Others asked the same question, though usually more diplomatically. I didn't really answer. Instead I shrugged and tossed out provocative topic changes. It's amazing how easily you can distract someone with the right question. Angie launched herself into a twenty-minute diatribe when I asked her if she and Jake, her latest, were really considering marriage. Some people can answer that question with a simple yes or no and a brief explanation. I knew Angie alternated between a rosy view of marriage as the joining of kindred souls and a darker vision of the institution as a systematic patriarchal plot to enslave women.

My friends were right. Michael did have it all. He was tall and lanky with the kind of style that carried off everything from blue jeans to a pin-striped suit. I once watched him turn on the charm for a tired, cranky bank teller. Her life's mission became giving Michael what he wanted, even though she was so flustered she could hardly count out the money. His quirky grin and ardently attentive eyes created more of an effect than plain old good looks ever would.

He came from a background of respected civic leaders. You'd probably know the family name if I told you. His upward mobility at the brokerage firm reflected his understanding of the rules of the stock market game.

As far as I knew, he'd been good at every sport he ever bothered to try. He even liked kids and petted stray dogs.

Then there was me. Saying that I came from an off-beat family was like saying the Indians should have gotten more for Manhattan than a few trinkets. First there was my name, Glory, the product of my mother's voracious reading habits. If I'd been born a few months earlier, during Mother's English novel stage, I'd be answering to Winifred. Hearing the other choices made living with the name Glory a lot easier. In fact, if the poet who inspired my mother's final choice hadn't been dead for fifty years, I'd probably be sending him Christmas cards.

If you followed consistent, clamoring protest groups for whom no cause was too small, you've heard of my family. You certainly wouldn't connect them with any mainstream civic activities. I'm not upwardly mobile, but there was a good chance that I'd decide what I wanted to do with my life pretty soon.

I am tall, like Michael, with everything in more or less the right places. The difference is that I'm skinny. Not slender but skinny. I remembered smuggling a Barbie doll into our politically correct household. I locked myself in my room with the doll, took off my clothes, and compared our respective figures in the mirror. The comparison wasn't encouraging and I didn't trust puberty to handle the problem. I was right. On me, my clothes look like someone else bought them, someone shorter or fatter or maybe someone whose body included a few more topographical variations. I could look in the mirror, when fully clothed, and know something was wrong; I just didn't have the patience to get it right. Hence the appeal of the baggy jeans and T-shirts trend. Michael worked his magic there. For a time I was as well dressed as Cinderella at the ball.

Now *you're* asking, what was I thinking when I dumped this great guy? Well, I did read as much as my mother and I had an active imagination. That, combined with a healthy dose of common sense, lay behind my decision. Let's start with the airport.

I've always loved the movement and colors in airports and that night was no exception. Planes took off and landed, taxied to and from runways. People walked in every direction. Some lagged under the weight of the day while others moved fast, frequently checked their watches, and dragged resisting children in their wake. Near collisions happened at the arrival and departure monitors. Bored airport attendants steered courtesy carts deftly around moving or stationary obstacles. Under the bright, relentless lights, brilliant colors jumped out of posters promoting exotic destinations. People waited expectantly. There was no better place to people-watch. I had been saying something like that, about people-watching, to Michael, when he said, "Let's be a story ourselves."

We were there with some friends, Angie, Jake, and another couple, to pick someone up. I don't remember why the group of us had decided to continue a night on the town with the funky flourish of an airport run. The idea lost its sparkle when fog delayed the flight arrival time by a couple of hours. Everyone started grumbling. Anyway, Michael grabbed my hand and pulled me off to the far side of the central concourse. He laid out his plan and it seemed innocent enough, if a bit silly. Michael rejoined the group, and as his scheme dictated, I wandered on through some little shops. The variety of airport stores surprised me with choices extending well beyond magazines, candy, tacky ashtrays, and mugs. You could buy all kinds of clothing at exorbitant prices and some of the clothes didn't even have a city or state name splattered across them. Twenty minutes later, at the far end of the concourse, threading my way through a crowd of people, I heard my name. Michael's voice broadcast the opening lines of our impromptu performance.

"Glory?" he said. "Glory? Is that you?"

I turned around and there he stood, with a huge grin on his face. He rushed toward me with open arms, gave me a big bear hug topped by a long passionate kiss, and then swung me around in a little celebration dance. Giggling, I held on for the ride.

"It's been so long and I couldn't believe it was really you. God, it's good to see you. Say you have some time. Here, let me take your bag. Come have a drink with me. Are you just passing through? Could you stay for a while?"

I laughed and nodded through Michael's barrage of words and another exuberant hug or two. At the same time I saw that we had attracted quite an audience of smiling, approving faces. Here and there, someone nudged their neighbor and made a comment. Michael's plan succeeded. He said that an airport was a totally believable place for an unexpected reunion. We would entertain the crowd and ourselves, while we waited. Of course, our friends witnessed the "reunion." Michael talked Angie and Jake into staging a similar scenario on a distant concourse, so they weren't playing to the same audience. Michael's awareness of his audience equaled that of any professional actor.

Now you could ask, What was the big deal? We had a

little harmless fun. The atmosphere of the airport inspired the moment and Michael coincidentally had that big old briefcase along that I carried as a suitcase. And, of course, if you noticed that I went along with the whole thing, you're right. But none of that mattered at that point. It was only the beginning. Or at least a beginning for me. I doubt that the same was true for Michael.

We'd go for weeks doing the usual things that couples do and then his penchant for staging events would surface. I grew wary, not that it made much difference. One night we were out for dinner at a restaurant, one of those ultra-chic nouvelle cuisine places that sprang into existence overnight. The muted rose-colored booths, arranged for maximum privacy, coordinated with the lush floral design of the carpet. Here and there, tiny spotlights lit up either a piece of art or a very understated bit of greenery in an exotically shaped vase. The food on our plates, meticulously arranged, looked more like art than anything edible. The other diners matched the subdued but expensive decor. Michael had been exceptionally attentive. Even though I occasionally suspected it took deliberate effort on his part, Michael made me feel clever and beautiful. He asked questions in the right places, laughed at my smallest jokes, and was a master of the seemingly casual little touches that heightened physical awareness. That night Michael broke the spell when he leaned toward me and said, "Throw your glass of water in my face."

I laughed but he took off from there. Raising his voice, he said, "God, don't laugh at me like that. I mean it this time, it'll never happen again. I've learned my lesson. You've managed to forgive me before, please, please . . . just one more time."

Speechless, I knew everyone else in the restaurant was either outright staring, or had at least stopped eating so they wouldn't miss what happened next.

"Say something, say anything. Please, say you still love me," he continued.

Every bit as angry as the supposedly wronged woman in his game, I coldly said, "I'm warning you, Michael, stop this right now."

"But darling, I swear I've stopped. It will never happen again. Just give me one more chance."

I stood and headed for the door hearing his final dramatic plea half-shouted at my back.

"No, no . . . don't leave me. Oh my God, what have I done?"

Presumably, he stumbled from the restaurant like a broken man, but when he caught up with me, Michael was jubilant.

"You were great! Everyone in the restaurant looked as bored as the wallpaper, but now they have something to talk about."

"I wasn't playing, Michael, and I don't plan on being a part of any more of your games."

A dramatic exit statement, but our relationship didn't end there. I've thought a lot about what kept pulling me back to Michael, despite my exasperation with his scenes. I met him when I was ultraconscious of my unconventional upbringing. Michael represented a traditional lifestyle with a twist. As much as I was drawn to the mysteries of yuppiedom, the realities would have probably been boring with anyone other than Michael. And, I have to admit, he flat out courted me and I fell for it. Courted is a silly, old-fashioned word, but nothing else fits. His repertoire included surprising me with flowers for no particular reason, comparing my eyes to stars, writing me bad poetry, toasting me with champagne, boating by moonlight, and generally suggesting that I was the center of his universe. When I wasn't furious with him, I was delirious with the first throes of love, or maybe just delirious.

The restaurant incident definitely taught Michael that I didn't have to be willing, to play my part to perfection. One gorgeous spring day, he swooped in and carried me off to the park. He brought a huge, old-fashioned picnic basket, complete with a red-and-white checked tablecloth, and filled with goodies. The food and the sunshine made me drowsy. Michael wandered off to see if the Frisbee was still in the trunk of his car. When I woke up I discovered some kind of search was under way. All around me voices called, "Bozo, Bozo." One little boy concentrated on small bushes, intently poking each one with a stick. A couple of older boys used the search as an excuse to wade through the brush at the edge of the little creek that flowed through the park. For a few minutes I couldn't see Michael, but I discovered him directing a young couple off toward the playground. Worried and more than a little curious as to who Bozo was, I stood up and started in his direction. In contrast to the concerned faces of the searchers, he was grinning. He explained it all. Bozo wasn't a who. Bozo was a what, my lost puppy to be exact. I hadn't had a dog since I was twelve and it wasn't named after some outdated clown. That time I didn't bother arguing; I walked away. I have no idea how he explained my lack of interest in the search, but I'm sure it was creative.

Over the next weeks, Michael called a lot, sometimes apologizing and sometimes chatting like everything was fine. He sent more flowers and poems along with sad looking stuffed dogs. One night, he had me serenaded by a mariachi band. When he promised to reform and to send the band away, I gave in again.

About a week later, Michael called one morning and invited me out to brunch. He said we were celebrating and suggested that I wear an upscale pseudo sailor outfit that he'd previously introduced into my wardrobe. We did go to brunch, though he explained the celebration.

On the way home, he took a different route. Almost everyone has passed a house that is so interesting from the outside that you want to see if the inside is as intriguing. This house was white-swirled stucco with brown shutters and a curved, rounded, shingle roof straight out of a fairy tale. It didn't take much imagination to wonder if it was made of gingerbread. I half-expected to see Snow White along with a dwarf or two pop out of the door. But it wasn't a cottage. Instead, it fell somewhere between a gingerbread house and a gingerbread palace. Surrounded by a tall hedge on three sides, the open front afforded a full view of lush rosebushes. The only detail that didn't fit the picture was the realtor's open house sign in a prominent position at the curb.

I objected as soon as Michael stopped the car and turned off the engine. He brushed off my objections, saying we were just going to take a quick look. The real estate agent, stationed right inside the door, definitely perked up when we walked in. I suppose we looked like the perfect young couple for the house. Michael took over, turned on the charm, and carried out the introductions. In short order, Mrs. Gillespie, the real estate agent, was salivating. According to Michael, we'd just gotten engaged and our financial circumstances carried us past the starter home stage directly into buying a real house, particularly something as unique as this. Short of calling my supposed fiancé a liar right there, I couldn't do much but smile and trail along for the tour. The inside of the house did live up to the promise of the outside. Odd patterns in the wood floors and curving walls made the transitions from room to room feel like popping through a looking glass. Encouraged by Michael's interest, Mrs. Gillespie grew more and more animated as she described the features of the house. It didn't end there. After we'd been on a full tour, Michael got the details of the financial picture as well. Finally, fed up, I made an excuse to escape to the car. Michael nabbed me as I walked by, tucked me neatly by his side, and went into his "oh gosh" routine.

"I'm sorry, Mrs. Gillespie, but I think everything is moving a little fast for Glory. I'll have to get her home for a rest. But here's my card, give me a call in the morning and I'll send a messenger over for those papers you mentioned. Of course, we'll need to talk with Glory's father as well. He's set on giving his little girl's marriage the best start possible," he said patting my stomach suggestively.

Somewhere in the middle of that speech, he'd handed the woman a business card and we were out the door.

At the car, tears threatened to water my anger down to a soppy ineffectiveness. Clinging to the anger I said, "What was that? You've got Mrs. Gillespie not only believing that we're engaged but that we're gonna buy that house. And I definitely didn't appreciate that last hint that little Glory was pregnant and the wedding better happen soon. We are, by the way, definitely not pregnant or engaged!" I didn't want Michael to know I was hurt, so I shifted away from the emotional impact of his foray into the real estate. "What exactly are you going to tell her when she calls tomorrow?"

He shrugged and opened the door for me. "She won't reach anyone. That was one of the cards the printer messed up. It just had my name and the phone number was wrong."

I hissed, "She's not stupid, she'll call information and get the brokerage firm's number."

As he slid in behind the wheel, he flashed me a brilliant smile and said, "I don't think so. She doesn't even know that I'm a stockbroker, much less where I work. My home number isn't exactly listed. Think about it."

Why did I dump him? Well, the commonsense answer is that I wanted something real. I wasn't sure that I'd ever want a man to get down on his knees and ask me to marry him. But if a man ever said, "Glory, will you marry me?" I wanted to know that it was a real question and not entertainment for the dinner crowd. In Michael's version of a proposal scene, clowns would pop up right after he popped the question. Each clown would carry floppy flower bouquets, wear an earnest expression, and shout, "No, marry me!" Everyone would have a good laugh.

The overactive-imagination answer is a kind of extension of the Michael proposal fiasco I envisioned. I had a timely realization the day after we met Mrs. Gillespie, by then a disappointed real estate agent. I was shopping for a birthday gift for my niece. At her mother's suggestion, I was looking for a game. In my experience toy departments are fun and aggravating. I always hear my mother's voice, "Glory, you don't have to pick out a doll. Look at these great tractors over there." As a child, I discovered that puzzles were the perfect neutral choice. Either that or games. Have you ever noticed how the games in stores are organized? At one end, you have games for small children like Candyland. As you progress up the aisle, you see Twister, Junior Monopoly, and Risk. Near the end of the section, you'll find chess, Taboo, and Trivial Pursuit, more complicated games for older children or adults. By the time you're playing chess, there isn't much chance that you'll want to go back to Candyland. Michael is an adult. What kind of games come after "Restaurant Drama," "Enticing Strangers into Looking for Bozo, the Nonexistent Puppy," and "House Hunting with My Fiancée, Glory, a Poor, Pregnant, Little Rich Girl"? My imagination supplied an avalanche of answers to that question. Most of the answers weren't much fun for anyone other than Michael or his audience.

I did remember my niece's birthday before I left the store. I bought her a doll that walked, a yellow dump truck with a hand crank to tip the back up, and a Wizard of Oz puzzle featuring Dorothy at her optimistic best. My niece can decide what game she wants to play and so can I.

for my grandmother i caught

1

this poem is
for my grandmother i caught
looking young in a photograph
you have 500 names
and still i can't call you abuelita
because i am too old
and you are not that old

2

this poem is
for my young grandmother
i caught looking
in a photograph you remind me of blue and yellow
progresso bean cans and shirts that read puerto rico
in a collection of cursive rainbows
i am fascinated by your orange peels

cha

this poem is for my looking grandmother
i caught young
in a photograph
you do not give closets
to only shoes
but to things that clutter your eyes
hector rivera

records and maybe even
his piano
        cha
this young poem
is for my photograph
grandmother i caught
looking
you and your serious insides
you leave me
to my earth
and remind me of all we don't finish
by dying

LINDA MILLER-KNOWLTON

from Portraits

Mary T.—*Atlanta, 1950*

Lawd, child money
Would be alright
I think I could be a
Friend to it
If it ever comes around
To call

Leslie's Feet—1990

My feet have carried me long.
Light with hope and heavy with child.
Quickly to approaching love
And painfully away
The heels resting on beds,
Sometimes in joy
Once in a while, not.
Through the years
Through the years
Of my life.

They look tired sometimes
And sometimes pretty.
Sometimes I can see my life
In them.

ANDREW RUTHERFURD

Chernozyem

"Comrade Sergeant, I will tell you what I told you before. I have never seen this man; he was standing behind me in this line for the butcher and I heard him shuffling his feet." The fat man looked around for others to confirm this. One large woman pursed her lips and nodded. The sergeant took her name. The fat man continued.

"Anyway, he tapped me on the shoulder, like this." The sergeant stiffened and the fat man apologized. "I turn around to look at him and he stumbles backwards, looking as if he has just seen a ghost. He clutches his chest and falls to the ground, people start to panic, and I kneel over him to find out what is the matter. He was gasping for air, about to die and—strangest thing—he reaches up and grabs my coat with a wild look in his eyes, pulls me close and says one word before he goes."

The sergeant's eyes narrowed and he nodded for the fat man to proceed.

" 'Golchik.' That was all he said, and then—" The man shrugged. "I do not know who he was talking about."

The police sergeant turned to the crowd. The body had already been removed to the hospital.

"Did anybody know this man, this"—he flipped back a page—"Arkady Sergeevich Ivanov?" There was silence. That night at the station he checked the name that the man had uttered, but there was no such name in the city, at least not anymore. The search for surviving relatives was also unsuccessful. He then duly noted that Arkady Sergeevich Ivanov had left this world on November the twenty-fifth, 1978. Briefly he wondered what that must be like, to leave no one behind. The sergeant went home to his family. It had been a long night. Someone else would see to it that the old man was buried, so he forgot the matter.

The trains were long, like a huge wall that rolled across the land. Trees were broken and fields burned away. The land was peppered with craters and dazed survivors who wandered about. The war was over and the men were singing with their bellies full, on their way home. They had been members of the Sixth Guards Army and had fought their way into Berlin, reducing the city to rubble as so many of theirs had been. Sometimes the cars were quiet with sleep and reflection. It was summer and flies were buzzing around the room. In the corner of one such car Private Arkady Sergeevich was having trouble sleeping. His legs were cramped and he did not wish to disturb the snoring soldier who was equally cramped in front of him. He wanted to be left alone and so he did not move.

He thought of Koza, who had been killed just before the battle for Kharkov, a year or so before. The Mongol was gentle, filthy, and abrupt, proud, disgusting, and funny; all the things that Arkady was not.

They were on an exercise in training when Arkady had run into a tree. Sitting in a daze and presumably alone, he had heard someone giggle. Turning, he saw the Mongol, whose giggle became a cackle when he saw Arkady's pained glare.

"Asshole," Arkady had said.

"There are too many trees to run up and hug them all," the man said, laughing. Soon Arkady was laughing too. Koza sat for a while and then declared that they should have a meal for their laughter. He rose and went off into the trees, only to return some time later with a small fish and some berries. Arkady shared his cigarettes and they became friends.

Koza was a herder who, it seemed to Arkady, excelled at everything. He told Arkady that it was because he was bored easily and that he had no tolerance for something done poorly. The officers recognized his talent and his popularity but not his sense of humour. This fact was utterly lost on Koza, who thought that some things were universal.

* * *

Their patrol was moving out of the woods. A field of wheat stretched out to their left, meeting the sky in the rolling distance. The same woods lay in a crescent to their right, Arkady heard the wind pushing through the trees. The autumn air was crisp, cooling his aching lungs after their fast march. It was late afternoon; the sun lay low in the sky before them. He knew that they had two or three miles before they reached camp and at this point he didn't care about anything else.

There were German reconnaissance groups in their area that they were supposed to find, reporting the locations of larger groups if possible. Koza had been in a foul mood since they had started, arguing the stupidity of sending such a large group out to look for small, alert squads of the enemy. In the end he went along, saying that doing something was better than nothing at all.

They walked single file, tired and dusty, stopping when the sergeant decided to take a short cut through the field. Arkady, of course, did not complain. Turning back before he left the trees he saw Koza look to their right and mutter something while shaking his head. Arkady began to walk, cursing his feet under his breath, hypnotized by the plodding boots in front of him. He was thinking of the cold sea when he was struck. In an instant, lying on the ground he felt his arm thickly aching and the blood pounding in his ears. All around him men were being killed—one by one it seemed—men he recognized but did not know. It all was happening outside him with unimaginable speed, while within him the world was stuck in glue. The sergeant who had taken them into the field was caught square by the German machine guns. He was flipping grotesquely across the path like a fish thrown onto land. Others ahead were jerking, puppets thrown to the ground. Arkady cringed. The withering fire from the woods had caught them all unaware, killing the men in front of Arkady. He could not turn and see how those behind him fared. He tried to push his body into the ground and disappear, wriggling as low as possible. *We will all die here,* he thought. *It will end now.*

"Here, in this fucking field, trapped like rats," he muttered. Disgust, that was what he felt, that and sadness—a great sadness. His fear kept him hugging the black earth, the *chernozyem. This is what the Nazis wanted, the rich soil of the Ukraine, this is what we are dying to save.* He looked up at the sergeant, bullets punching him around, *and they're welcome to it.* Arkady heard sobs and groans through the bursting of the guns and the bullets' whine. Dying men calling for comfort from their mothers. They had all done so as children waking from troubled sleep. He saw the blood spreading from his wounded shoulder—felt the throbbing, his heart pounding out of its cage.

"It is useless." He felt tears. He was crying into the dust.

In a flash he was pulled up to his feet and pushed forward. Koza had appeared from behind him, his gun in one hand and the other gripping Arkady's arm. His eyes were wide with a blood lust, his jaw clenched, and his lips pulled back.

Arkady noted later that at that moment, Koza more resembled a bear than a man—he *was* snarling. When he did tell this to Koza, the Mongol laughed but said nothing.

They ran wordlessly under Koza's aegis for the trees straight ahead, to flank the Germans. The two made an odd pair; Koza was churning like an attacking beast and Arkady was stumbling, his head light and his arm useless.

Yet they made it to safety. Arkady slumped against a tree and slid to the ground, exhausted from his fear.

"You'll be fine," Koza said tersely.

What was left of their squad was beginning to inch its way towards the Germans, preferring to remain on their bellies but at least heartened by Koza enough to return fire.

"I left my gun," Arkady said quietly. He looked up to see Koza's reaction, but he was gone. Arkady could barely see him running at a crouch through the woods—towards the Germans.

Seeing the Mongol getting silently drunk afterwards, Arkady somehow knew that Koza valued the life of a friend more than who won a fight, perhaps even more than his own life. He could not have cared less if no one had seen him do it. Arkady was struck by this—more so because he was not sure that he had the same strength. It burned him. The answer was in him somewhere, in some dark corner. Koza did not even have to ask that question to himself. He was pure. Koza told Arkady that he would be all right and Arkady believed him.

When Koza died, Arkady had gone back within. Some men when they lost their friends found it easier to make other friends and bond with their comrades. Arkady had no friends before Koza and so he stuck his neck out for no one after. There were times when he fought hard, but Koza was a better soldier than he, braver and more competent. Once, however, Arkady had been brave.

Dawn was less than an hour away and the vodka, cold as the stars, was flowing. Fires burned up and down the line as men sang, their voices rising to a single roar of many songs from many places. The air was sharp in the vast expanse of snowy hills. The Sixth Guards Army lay thirty miles north of Kharkov. Their attack on the German's position atop the hill would, if successful, cut off the enemy's supply lines. The men did not care; they were drunk and warm from the fires and they wanted a fight.

Arkady sat dazed by the effects of the vodka while several feet away, Koza lay splayed out, vomiting in the snow. Arkady chuckled and Koza turned back, smiling, his beard speckled with bits of food.

"Hungry?"

"No thank you, Koza." He heard the popping of the artillery behind him and waited for the shells to hit the German positions. "Wipe your face off before you talk to me, oaf."

Koza thumbed his nose, grinning. "Give me more." Arkady threw him another bottle from the crate. It did not matter, within the hour they would be running, howling towards the Nazis. If Koza was drunk, that was good for him. The commissar was yelling at someone up the line, threatening to report the person. He was Ivan Golchik, the group's political officer, a fat, pasty, and dangerous man, so frightened of the party that he would kill for it. He called himself Ivan the Terrible. The men called him Ivan the Simpleton yet they picked up their guns all the same.

"Five minutes!" Golchik was shrieking. Some laughed nervously as they rose and shouldered their weapons. Others merely stood silently, their minds far away. The postmaster was also approaching. Arkady had no letters to send home and so he looked away, uncomfortably, towards the hill. Many shells had fallen short of the Germans. Arkady groaned and loaded his gun. Turning, he saw Koza sleeping in the snow, still smiling and twitching in a dream. He kicked snow onto his face.

"Koza, wake up." Koza muttered something that Arkady could not understand and did not budge. "Koza. Wake *up!*" he said, knowing that the Simpleton was on his way over and was loading a revolver, as he usually did before a charge. Arkady rubbed the fog out of his glasses. "Idiot. You will be shot."

"Get away, you little girl."

Arkady laughed nervously as Ivan approached. The light was breaking, and the mortars were popping furiously. Arkady, standing above his drunk friend, turned to meet him.

"Report, Private. Why won't he get up?"

"Can't you see? He is drunk and he will not budge." He added, "Give him a second, he is a good man."

"I have no time for anyone, boy," Ivan sneered. He stood above Koza and cocked his revolver. Koza's eyes opened from the familiar sound and he gave Ivan a level stare.

"Rise!" Ivan screeched.

"Comrade Commissar." Koza spat out the words. "Fuck off please and let me sleep." Ivan's eyes bulged out of his head and Arkady stood, in suspended animation, as Koza added, "I am happy right here."

One hollow shot rang out and Arkady's innards froze. He stared in disbelief, unable to accept the truth. Koza's eyes were open and glazed. The sun was coming up as Golchik swaggered down the line, yelling something about cowards and an example. The other men were staring at Arkady. No one said a word. Arkady's rifle fell from his hands. He picked it up and found himself walking with slow, purposeful steps after Golchik; his hands clenched around the weapon. He felt their eyes upon him and did not care. *I will die today,* he told himself and he met the thought with ambivalence. Golchik had not turned. The troops were ready to charge; the mortars had stopped.

Somewhere he heard a whistle blow, followed by a thousand others. A great roar arose, and with that, the Sixth Guards Army was upon the Germans.

Arkady saw Golchik during the confusion of the charge and ran nearby. When they were close enough to German lines he put the fat man on the other end of his barrel and shot him in the head. Golchik fell face-first in the snow and did not move. Arkady paused long enough to roll him over onto his back where he could see that some of the right side of his face was missing. Satisfied, he ran on.

When the attack was successful, Arkady expected that someone would inform on him out of fear for retribution upon the entire battalion. No such thing happened. It was a silent tribute to how hated the political officer had been. One or two veterans told Arkady to keep his head low anyway. It seemed that he had acquired a new status, as a madman of sorts. He was left alone and given leeway among them to sit where he wished. He chose to sit outside the circle.

God protects children and fools, Arkady said to himself as he sat, stuffed into his corner. He watched the others sleep, talk, play cards, and sing, grateful that he was not one of them. An hour or so ago they had been given a large, hot meal when they had exchanged their weapons. He was full for what he felt to be the first time in years. Sometime soon they would arrive in Voronezh, where they would disembark, part company, and take their trains home. Soon he could put these years behind him. Arkady felt his eyelids dropping; he smiled to himself.

"Finally," he said, and slept.

> The sand fell away as he and his father put out to sea. The ocean absorbed the cries of the seagulls; seaweed and the fine salt mist filled the air. No ships on the horizon, only the ghost of an island and birds diving in their wake. The beach behind them was barren, thunderheads were rumbling, and the black waves, crashing ceaselessly, pulled the sand into their dark embrace. Arkady and his father rose and fell over the sea, pulling the nets up, hand over callused hand. They were heavy; "The catch must be good," he heard his father say. At last they heaved nets onto the deck, and there among the fish lay Koza, a bullet hole in his forehead.

Arkady awoke with a jolt. The train was quiet, the others were sleeping off their meals. *I must not think of Koza,* he told himself, although he knew that with the war over and Koza dead, it would be easier to think of nothing at all. There was little to do but sleep, however, as they had not arrived, so Arkady slept and this time was careful not to dream.

The train did not stop in Voronezh; it continued northeast to the dismay and confusion of all aboard. There was speculation that became suspicion when the rations were stopped with no word why. Several men tried to jump off the train and found that the huge doors had been bolted shut. There was panic; fights broke out for no reason. They were quick and dirty jobs on one man, usually by several that ended with a sobbing man who was crying from more than just the beating. Arkady kept out of trouble by lying in the corner and not speaking to a soul. The car began to really stink after days of rolling on. They had descended into purgatory, none knew where he was going or why, and old scores were settled in the darkness. Eventually they were all weakened and tired, disoriented. In this state, as intended, they reached the Gulag.

When he left the train, Arkady saw armed guards and dogs, a road stretching into the woods, and land as flat as ice. It was summer. Flies and mosquitoes filled the air.

"Why have they done this?" he heard someone ask. "What did we do?"

At that moment a colonel spoke over a loudspeaker, instructing them to proceed in an orderly manner behind the truck along the road and to await instructions.

"What is happening?" one man cried out. Another said, "This is wrong." The man with the microphone ordered them to be quiet or they would be punished.

"For what!?" a soldier whom Arkady knew shouted. The guards approached him quickly, there was a scuffle, and he was removed, bloodied and cursing. No one saw where he was taken and he was not seen again. Several minutes passed until a rifle sounded from the woods and the men saw birds take flight from the sound. Nobody spoke on the way to the camp; the air was humid and Arkady felt sick with hunger. They walked for maybe eight miles through the woods and all that time he stared at the feet of the man in front of him, to keep from passing out. Their destination was a barbed-wire enclosure of long wooden buildings and high guard towers, stern guards, and large, angry dogs. Arkady thought that this must be a long and detailed nightmare and he never really lost that first impression. They received bread, porridge, and water in exchange for their uniforms, and from that point on they were no longer soldiers of different rank but prisoners of the labour camp.

Their days began with a small meal, after which they

went to work in the summer making cement in a limestone quarry and in the winter, chopping trees. It was numbing and bleak; even the bravest had no stomach to rise up. Arkady kept his head down, as always, trusting none and talking only occasionally to another for some contact. He needed only a small dose to remind himself that he was human and to remain sane; yet gradually it mattered to him less and less and finally, not at all. All of the prisoners dissolved into one gaunt and pale creature, flesh sucked up by the Arctic cold and ribs like dead trees, fingers like branches. Eyes like a bird's nest. The world was indeed upside down and each did what he could to survive, whether that meant to be in a group or, in Arkady's case, alone. The nights were quiet and he slept without dreams. Each night would leave him with only enough energy for the next day.

And the days, the days crawled past. It had been years since Arkady had heard the strings of a balalaika, eaten a good meal, seen the sea of his youth. There had been a young man, a Georgian, who used to sing at night in their barracks. His voice was beautiful, too beautiful for these men, who cried quietly at its sound. He sang old songs that nobody knew. One winter morning he became sick and everybody except Arkady tried to help him by bringing him extra food and clothing. He died, however, and some grew angry with Arkady for doing nothing to help the sick man when he could. Arkady spoke for the first time in an age.

"You only cared because he sang!" he lashed out. "If he were ordinary, like me, you would have *taken* his clothes and food." There was silence. He continued, "I alone admit that I couldn't give a shit about him, dead or alive!"

Nobody bothered him after that, but a part of Arkady secretly missed the songs. Time began to pass him by; he lost track of it and so it returned the favour by losing track of him. His heart was withering from neglect; he no longer thought of music, the sea, food, freedom, or even Koza. He thought of nothing and so he became nothing. And then it happened, as it was bound to: Arkady's world was broken.

He had been part of a wood-chopping detail that was composed mostly of prisoners from another barracks. The wooded hills were grey in the northern winter's dark days. Arkady was eating a small lunch that he had saved from the previous night's dinner on the other side of the crest, where he thought he would be alone. He was resting, when he heard somebody yell at him to move. He looked up and saw a tree falling towards him and dove out of the way at the last instant. It crashed down beside him, throwing an explosion of snow into the air. He sat, dazed by the close call, and then he heard someone approaching. Arkady looked up at a man with a thin, disfigured face.

"You are lucky I saw you there," the man said.

"Thanks," Arkady replied although he felt strangely ungrateful.

"May I sit?"

"Mnn."

The prisoner sat near him. *Something about the eyes,* Arkady thought.

"I am Ivan Semyonovich Galstuk."

"Fat chance. Who has a last name that means 'necktie'?"

"Galstuk" laughed heartily. "Lighten up, friend, I just saved your life." Arkady chuckled for the man's benefit and not out of any sense of mirth. "Galstuk" then began to talk about how people should stick together and that they were all soldiers really. Just then they heard a sound from over the crest and when the man looked back to see what it could be, Arkady saw that he was missing his right ear.

"How did you lose your ear?"

"Excuse me?" the man replied. Arkady asked the question again. "Well you are a strange one." Arkady did not comment but he stared fixedly at the man now.

"I was wounded and left for dead at Kharkov."

"Who did you serve with?"

"The Sixth Guards Army. I was decorated there. Why do you ask?"

And he knew. He knew that this was for him the worst man in the world, the one who had killed his only friend. A cornered wolf struck out within Arkady. He felt as if his very body would split in two. His axe was too far away, so he felt his hands grab a branch from the fallen tree and tear it off. Golchik tried to scramble away but he slipped.

"I am the one," Arkady heard himself say and he lifted the branch high and began to hit Golchik with it. The second blow knocked him out and they continued to fall. He rained his fury upon his enemy until his eyes stared sightlessly at Arkady's through an ever thickening film. He only stopped when he could no longer summon the force to continue. Arkady dragged Golchik to the tree and dumped him beside it. The animal left him and he sank to his knees. All of the emptiness had seeped from his heart into his hands, where like a shadow, he could see it. His shoulders shook and he sobbed out many years for he had killed the man who had saved him, and what does a man do after that?

The night before he died, Arkady had a dream.

> He and his father are out on the sea under a pregnant, northern sky. The terns are falling, turning, and rising behind their boat. Beside them the foam, the white horses, charge across a dark land. Bitter winds howl

around their heads. Under them the strong water bucks and swells. He hears his father say, "She will not give today." Nevertheless they haul the nets in, hand over callused hand until they are almost upon the deck. Arkady leans over the side and sees Golchik in the net. Golchik reaches up and grabs Arkady, pulling him into the waves. They break through the net and Arkady is taken down, down into the cold, black water.

TIMOTHY JUHL

No Known Survivors

Joseph Was
used to hustle it
and when he'd grown tired
of too many tricks
and too many barstools, Joseph Was
crawled into my life
and did it for free.

. . . but you can call me Joey

Joseph Was
chewed spearmint gum
and smoked cigarettes for breakfast
at night his drink left sweating
on the coffee table, Joseph Was

crawled drunk to my room
and curled into me.

. . . call me Joey please

Joseph Was
had pale blue eyes
crazy-boy blue he'd say
as you splashed across them
in a glance then, Joseph Was
crawled into my bed
for something to hold.

. . . Joey please just Joey

Joseph Was
took off one morning
without combing his hair
said he missed the smell
of the sidewalk, Joseph Was
crawled into the night
and bled away.

. . . but you can call me Joey

In Silver

I have pictures
stolen from you.

Tall and
languorous in the
mercury glass
shimmer of a thousand
ornaments in a
shop window where
you stopped
and stared
and where you
glistened under
a shower of
tinsel tears.
Then I followed
your reflection in
the chrome of a
slow rolling
sedan a liquid
image stretching
the gap in
your stride.
The sight of
you flickering
watery in the glint of
slick city puddles
from last
night's storm.

And that curvy
glimpse of
you from the
bottom of my
teaspoon at
breakfast
this morning.
And then there's
the rain silver
like slivers as
I press cold
against the door
and watch
you go.

The Last Hours of Irene Grace

Old men
tiptoe to the bed
their soles caked with rich soil,
to the sister
stricken, almost mummified
poisoned yellow, almost petrified
they tiptoe and bow their heads
whisper old men prayers
and curses

at this thing so close
now
and rub weathered fingers
against the grit in their eyes.
In turn they pat her hand,
the skin cool and papery thin,
the veins and vessels
hieroglyphs;
they pat her hand,
gentle,
a farmer's touch;
mutter old words,
taste sand on their lips,
promises in these last hours
to take their sister home.

HILARIE AYERS

Reading and the Highlighter

The average college student carries the essentials of collegiate life in his backpack: a binder, some paper, pencils, pens, various textbooks, and a highlighter pen. The highlighter has become an important part of a student's learning routine. The click of the highlighter cap now accompanies the familiar scratch of pens and the drone of professors.

While the highlighter pen does aid in studying, it can be overused to the point of making it ineffectual.

Highlighter use tends to start in junior high. It begins as a status symbol. It shows that the student is no longer in elementary school and that he can now make pink and yellow marks on college-ruled paper. Use of the pen drops off in high school, mostly because students study less. But in college, the highlighter pen comes back in full force. In junior high and high school, more girls than boys have pens, but in college no self-respecting student would be without his highlighter. In every class students can be found highlighting their notes and their texts, in a rainbow of color, to mark items for future study. By skimming the text in this manner, looking only for main points and possible testable material, students are not learning to read effectively. Instead of reading to analyze ideas, students read to regurgitate information.

I consider myself more fortunate than most of my fellow students. I am able to read rather quickly and I am able to remember what I read. Because I read as fast as I do, I read a lot. I have learned to pick out the important parts of the text without the aid of a highlighter. I still have a highlighter, though. In fact, I have six: pink, yellow, green, blue, purple, and orange. And I use them regularly. Lately, I have highlighted on the hockey schedule the games that I want to go to this season. On the hockey team's training camp roster, I highlighted in purple the guys that I like. In pink, I highlighted the guys that I thought would make the teams, and last week, in blue, I marked my correct picks. (I didn't highlight the guys who didn't make it.) These pens are very handy.

I don't like to mark in my textbooks. I want to sell these books back and I'm always afraid that the bookstore won't take them back if they look too much like a rainbow. I know that I never buy a book that has been highlighted. Buying a highlighted book seems to me like peeking at someone's test paper. We might have the same questions on paper but his answer might be wrong. I don't want to copy that. Even if we have the same book, we might have different professors. We might think differently. He may have found the chapter on "Eighteenth-Century Women" terribly exciting and full of fascinating information while I do not. I cannot trust the highlighting judgment of a stranger. I can't sell my highlighted books and expect a stranger to trust mine.

If I use the highlighter at all when I study, it is usually to review my notes for a quiz or a test. I can first highlight the major topics I need to cover and then use a different color to mark my notes as I review. On an occasion when a professor allows a 3 × 5 card cheat sheet for a test, I never use the pen. The highlighter should be used to mark important information in the notes and the text. These highlighted bits should be written on the card. To rehighlight these main points and reminders is a sign of highlighter dependency.

I have known students who did not know when to stop with the highlighter. I think highlighting is a type of book graffiti. It's like scribbling E. L. WAS HERE on a brick wall; he made progress but it wasn't necessarily constructive. A student may leave a highlighter mark on each page of his text, but that is not evidence of learning. I have watched students cover entire pages with yellow or pink highlights. Sometimes they even alternate pink and yellow to mark the difference between the major points and the major, major points. Eventually, they can highlight a hole in the page. There is no learning taking place here: only coloring.

Because I am fortunate enough to be a natural reader who can learn and understand so easily, the highlighter is not as important to me as it is to others. I have pens and I use them, sometimes even for school purposes, but I am not dependent upon them to help me learn. For some students, the pen is the only easy way to remember what the professor wanted them to know. It might help these students if highlighters came with instructions on the back of the packages. Maybe the packages could say, "Only one paragraph of highlighted material is permissible per page." But then the students would not wear out their pens as quickly, so there is little benefit to the manufacturer in that.

Highlighter pens diminish the joy of reading. To read with a highlighter in hand is to consider only what the professor thinks about the material and to disregard what the reader thinks. And although there is little room for opinion on the function of the valves of the heart, it would be better for a student to think about the value of heart valves than to simply highlight their names in a textbook. Overuse of a highlighter is underuse of a mind.

If the highlighter pen is used sparingly and with restraint, I think that it can be useful for students who do not enjoy reading and who find studying difficult. I'm sure the pen will have a permanent place in the college student's backpack.

Now, I think I will go and highlight the games that my hockey team has won in yellow and the games they have tied in green. (I won't highlight the games they lost.)

JONATHAN VITAL

Father Drummer

I'm thinking about T.Rex
and trying to remember if Marc Bolan and the other guitarist
were the ones who committed the double suicide.
Two shotguns in an *X* and "1 . . . 2 . . . 3."

My father used to play *Bang a Gong* on his 8-track
and sing along while my mother held her ears and smiled
from the kitchen. "Dick, you can't sing."
I'd sit for hours listening and staring at the pictures
on album sleeves.
Men in leather pants, hair glowing
red
and blue
from stage lights.

"Were you ever in a band, Dad?"
And he told me about how,
at a fraternity party,
The Flamingos had played
and the drummer had passed out on Wild Turkey,
so he sat in.

I played him our record last year.
He laughed and told me he liked my fills.
"You're not as good as T.Rex," he said.
He sat down behind his old kit,

started playing along to the same
Ahmad Jamal record he'd had
since I could remember.
Banging away until
his shirt was dark with sweat.

My mother called me
and told me about her new job.
Her friends.
"He's drinking," she said.
I think of the dark room
at the back of his office.
Bed. tv.
drumset.

MARCY D. OLSON

Stellar Revelation

She is once again
awake
in the middle of this thing
we call night
she gazes at the stars
a splattering of glow-in-the-dark
stickers on the ceiling
she put up long ago knowing
it was the closest thing to romance

she could muster in this life
she plans
to take them with her when she leaves
she dreams of better
shoes
and other things she knows he can't give her
but he seems to think
he can do
well enough, for now, and for all she knows
he can, but she knows better
and knows it's not enough to wish it
or even make plans
she knows it's enough
for now, but now is so short
and then what?
A star loses its adhesive
and falls to the bed sheets
and she wishes she could make a wish
and know it would come true
if she wished it hard enough
but instead she stumbles through the dark
and gets her masking tape
She puts the star back in its place
in her make-believe sky
while he snores
You'd think he hung the moon
or something
only she knows better
she hung it herself
and she likes it that way.

BARBARA EGEL

Bra Shopping, Opus 36C

I shrugged myself into extra-strength lace
While you whistled through the flimsy pink door
Which I subtly nudged open a little more
Once the saleslady left. I wish your face
Could replace the satin bow between my breasts
(Which would nearly cover your ears). This close
To naked with you so near, I suppose
I want some guarantee that you're impressed.
It's not that I've fantasized fitting
Rooms (mirrors, maybe, but fluorescent lights?)
So until we're sated with long, sticky nights,
Tell me, love, how your insides are splitting
At the sight of me so bare.
                                        I am behooved
To buy the one most easily removed.

Nothings

The distilled sweetness of a single phrase
Sincerely spoken—"My Love," "My Treasure"—
Can send the sense careering all its ways
And launch the heart to heights confounding measure.

Yet racing blood's not warmed by words alone,
But by the instant that the lover's voice
Finds richer timbres—"My Heartsease," "My Own"—
And makes with small breath a breathtaking noise.

The cherished wear a mantle simply sewn,
Made of half-heard murmurs, whispers and small sighs,
That clothes the heart which by such sounds has grown
Too full for ordinary fineries.

Working Lunch

We hold our chopsticks ready to dissect
The typeface, pied and squared as samurai,
Amid which sits the frosted pink fish flesh.
Some rice grains fall and scatter on the page
Like living scansion marks in *bas-relief.*
This table's packed with too much protein:
Sesame and language—concentrated, rich.
The wild tangles of tentacle and kelp
Are delicate and clean and pared, like verse
Split by the cleaver of a Zen-chef.

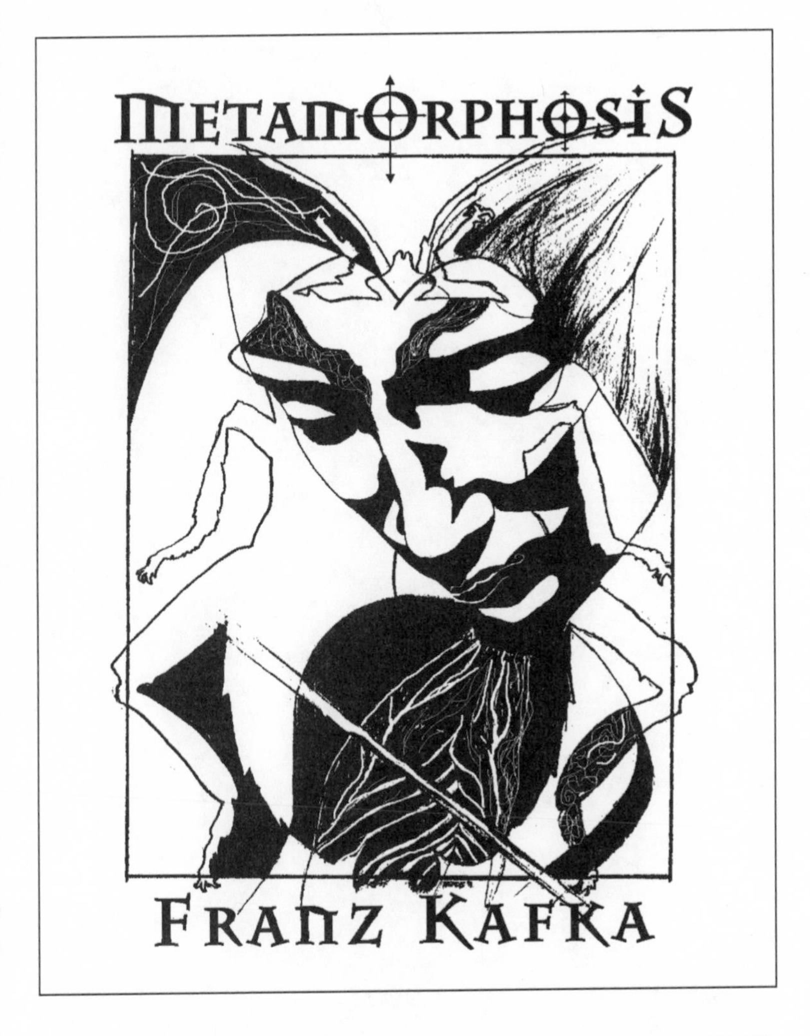

Franz Kafka/The Metamorphosis CHRIS PARADIS

JAN QUACKENBUSH

Stone Eggs

I figured Daddy's muskrat trap could snap a weasel's head right off. I took the trap down off a hook in the cellar, scraped it clean in the yard, sniffed it—rust and last winter's blood—and got to feel my own blood surge thick and strong. I surely felt a lot older than twelve. I needed to, I was in charge of the farm a few days. Daddy, Momma, and sick, little Ben, were gone over to LeRaysville—a funeral. One of Momma's Mennonite relatives. "Mind the eggs," Momma said. "Guard the coop," said Daddy. And start chores early—which meant everything imaginable: taking eggs, watering the hens, turning them out, weeding the garden, and such—I could cook if I wanted to, or eat cold.

"But mind smokin' the stove," Daddy said, remembering some green sticks one recent morning when I'd mispicked from an unseasoned pile—the stove stuffed full and gagging us all.

"Oh, Sam," Momma said, giving me a wink, "don't he know his lesson?" I felt Momma bestowing some faith in me; I waved the egg pail and blushed, my family fading as the pickup reversed out the lane. Next morning it looked a creature had struck the chickens my first night alone, and I guessed it was a weasel.

With a stick poked into the ring of the trap's chain, I started swinging the humped metal over my head, whistling and tramping along the grassy trail for the coop, singing "You're a poor dead sucker mister weasel"—as I was certain I would kill him: the varmint who had gutted a hen in the coop.

A gray, weathered coop made of rough-cut hemlock boards, set up on creosoted posts sawn from old rural electric poles. A mound of chicken crud stood under the trapdoor in the floor where we had shoveled it in wintertime—birds indoors all day. The breeze blew the stink smack up my nose, so I hurried up, scooping handfuls of earth and spreading it around to look natural; then with a chunk of shale rock I pushed the trap's heel down hard so the jaws opened up. I flattened them wide apart with my foot, lifted the disc tray, and clicked it back into the groove that cocked the trap. Weasel was going to lose his head quick. I would skin him and give it to Daddy, show him a killer I'd salted and turned into just a measly old rag.

"How do, Old Willie?" I called out, easing my foot lightly down on the cinder block he had for a porch step. I smashed a mosquito landed on my forehead, then leaned on a knee, looking to better see Momma's second cousin once removed, Old Willie, mostly a stranger to me—a gaunt man who drew water from the creek then disappeared back into the woods. This was the first time I visited his cabin, my first close sight of him. He sat on an upturned flour cask deep within his porch, against the chinked log wall. Sun was already halfways up, slanting through trees around us. In the shadows he looked slack—a gunnysack on a rail in the barn. There was barky smoke from his pipe; a pile of split cedar wood aside his door. "It's me, Old Willie," I said to him. "Tommy."

"Ye Thomas, ye say?" he asked as he drew up a pant leg and reached to scratch a bitten shin—sending off a blackfly.

"That's me," I sailed out, glad he sounded friendly.

"Well, c'mon here and set, Thomas."

I pulled two fresh chicken heads from my overall pockets, and, laying them right down on his lap, I said: "Look it here, Old Willie." He squinted—some seventy years old—"What ye got here?" he asked. His lips curled back and I saw his teeth were yellow nubs, small kernels, worn from grinding. I explained to him that a weasel had gotten past my trap and into the coop. Well, pretty soon, he told me it wasn't no weasel, but a possum.

In my second visit over to Willie's cabin, I dropped a chicken carcass onto his lap. His face went wrinkly as a small gray cabbage, and I noticed the pockmark craters underneath his whiskers—a pox Willie'd had as a kid. Momma once told it.

"Shoo, what's this, Thomas?"

I answered him saying it was another killed bird from the coop, told Willie that this time both legs had been ripped off, and no sign of them anywheres. And that I found it at daybreak, and now the coop was down to eleven hens left, and how could it be the possum, which he'd told me to bait for using a liver, since the bait was untouched, the trap wasn't sprung.

"So what can be doing it, Old Willie?" I asked, dismayed.

Momma had said Old Willie was simpleminded. She'd spoke in a scolding tone: Old Willie had married, then later ran off silly with a girl. And that was the cause why Willie had lost the farm, before she and Daddy took it over, as the other Mennonites had shunned him. When Willie returned—alone and ashamed—Momma out of kindness told him he might could build in the woods. She told me old Willie then learned to know up close almost every living creature: attitude and what not. So I was now trusting him for a keen answer.

He said a *bear:* "Ye got a bear into the coop, Thomas."

"A bear? Do bears eat chicken, Old Willie?" I asked plain surprised, as I'd never heard such'thing. I shivered, head to toe. "How can I fight off a hungry bear?" I asked, it being impossible, surely. I was growing fast but I wasn't large, yet.

"Douse ye hens in Epsom salts, make a brine," he said. "Deer will, but bear don't eat salt." Old Willie then set a match to his pipe. He seemed terribly smart in secrets of creatures. He himself had long, pointy fingernails, and a sharp, powerful smell, like boiled mustard greens, or vinegared horseradish root—a man who knew wilderness.

The hens I caught one by one using a four-foot, wooden leg catcher—hooked the curved end around the legs to snare them. The birds got piled in a gunnysack and brought to the kitchen where I soaked each real good in Momma's porcelain basin; even their heads went under. Afterwards I let the birds run crazy in the yard, when they hid in the bordering blackberry brambles, too senseless to go try and nest. Up at the coop, I dipped their hatchy eggs, and next soaked the stone eggs. The drying sun left a white filmy coat of salt. I tasted it. I washed down the shed, too. Inside and out, both. My hands got papery. If I licked my knuckles they shone like crystals of ice. Worked all day at it, didn't get to the garden at all. Then when the sun was going down, I went off to the creek to fish, to cook for supper. *Trout,* I hoped.

The ripe elderberries stopped me on the path to the creek: fat, purple clumps that smelled like wild jam when it's cooking with sugar. The bushes were in a stand that seemed like a candy store having branches instead of shelves, with a door wide open. All I needed to do was to reach in safely past the owner: an orange-dotted orb-web spider watching me from his window of spun silk—I decided to use my fishing pole. And just when I'd snagged a wheel of good berries, up stood a black bear, twelve feet away in some bushes in front of me. I froze stiff. He was staring straight at me—eyes like small, black walnuts, jaws stained with purple juice—sniffing, in short bursts as if his snout could sip my odor. Then that spider jumped onto my wrist, causing me to jerk to shake it off, and with that the bear started snorting—fierce with laid-back ears:

"Yeow!" I hollered, running away for dear life. I lunged, speeding over root and rock toward the creek, where I shinnied up a sycamore tree, and sat straddling a fat limb over the water, which would make a bear think twice about drowning—if he came climbing up after me. I waited, watching as I peered through a window of leaves and listened, but no bear. I only saw crows wheeling through the woods, and the creek that flowed bubbling below me.

Darkness came on and I turned from fear to anger—mad at my cowardice. "You dang monster, bear!" I shouted, rocking my feet and kicking the air. "Eat salt and die!" In the sky, a near-full moon rode up, splashing silver into the creek. "Roll on," I told the moon. "Go find China." I felt stuck. Off a ways, a barred owl barked its eight hoots of twice-fours. I waited and watched until I felt I might doze off yawning and topple into the creek. Then I slid down the trunk for home, and stalked the path fearing a bear was waiting behind each tree.

"It's true, Old Willie, I swear it! I saw the bear right-dang face to face!"

This was the morning after I was treed, and old Willie grinned like he disbelieved the bear truly happened, while on Willie's lap was a fifth carcass, found in the coop at daybreak with the trapdoor wide open like all the world could come in, the crud heap showing and hen guts on the floor: all amounting to plain evidence of bear.

"Dang! dang! dang!" I blasted at Willie while stomping hard on a porch board. "Just look it; that's the dang bear's mess you're holding—*see* it?" Four nights, *five* dead birds—this one had legs but no breast, just cavity—as if Epsom salts had crazed the bear.

"Coon," said Old Willie, somberlike, his hand feeling around inside the cavity, a finger roaming over the neck spikes.

"Coon, Old Willie? A coon'll eat salted chicken?" Thumbs in pockets, I glanced down at a knothole. "I surely must have missed out getting told of it before now," I said. "It's sure a surprise."

"Love salt," answered Old Willie, plunging his hand deeper, up to the wrist. "Loves it even worse than his cousin does."

"What cousin? I've not heard once that raccoons have got cousins." Old Willie's hands commenced to split apart the bird's legs.

"Ye h'ain't?" he asked, cracking the hen's hip plate.

"Not as I recollect."

"See this toothpick?" he asked, suddenly pulling a white long needly thing from behind his ear.

"Sure, right well."

"Porcupine—cousin to coon," he winked. "Look ye here." He set the quill between his front teeth stubs and, flexing his lips, wrinkling his nose, he flopped it up and down.

"Heck," I laughed, "that's sure a dopey trick, old Willie."

But I just couldn't figure a coon: its strength if compared with the force any bear has. So I asked Willie about coons and latched doors. He tossed the dead chicken over to the firewood pile, sniffed his hands, then started a lesson so natural sounding it seemed learned from patterns of dots on box turtles' shells: Coons could lift door latch hooks since coons, born to climb and to open things, were gifted considerably, having thumbs and fingers. Coons grasped and pulled doors open, shimmied themselves into places with no trouble at all: tent flaps, chest lids, boxes, outhouse doors, coops—nothing ever was a problem to a coon hot for food, 'specially if salted food. And coons "scavenge—pry out small doses at a time," hissed Old Willie.

"Heck, I know it," I said right back. "I've seen coons messing." I had, too—creek, cornfield, garden, sorting their bits of food, cobs, cantaloupes, creek mussels—only not attacking hens, nor grabbing eggs, either.

"How about the wide-open trapdoor?" I asked. "That's surely bear, isn't it? It's heavy." I scuffed at the knothole in the board, polishing it with my leather sole.

"Bear was underneath," Old Willie replied right off, then quick whacked some feisty gnats at his scalp. "But when bear got a lick of them Epsom salts he had to quit—he never got inside like the coon through the door did."

"Oh," I said, quietly. I jimmied my toe into the knot-hole and twisted, making splinters. Old Willie pulled apart his pipe and started cleaning it, using the quill: poked it into the stem and out came chunks of leaf. I went to sit on the edge of the porch.

Counted: weasel, or possum, bear, coon—figuring it might next be porcupine. I had lost five Kintner Hatchery certified Rhode Island hens: good steady layers. I'd lost Momma a goodly batch of eggs she'd have sold. I was bound to get a scolding, as though I weren't minding the coop but swimming all day in the creek. While Momma and Daddy might like to believe me, still the fact was I had dead chickens.

Old Willie's pipe smoke meandered over; without looking up I said, "What you smoking, Old Willie, wet sawdust?"

"Burdock leaf."

"Burdock leaf?"

A red-tailed hawk fanned past a cedar and then swept upward for a high oak limb. I looked in wonderment, felt thrilled by its acrobatics, but all I largely thought about was that Old Willie smoked a plant I had always to yank from the garden and throw out.

My fingers digged at the soft edges of the porch boards. I wondered if in being terribly disappointed Momma and Daddy would throw me out, sending me off for another while at Uncle Schaeffer's—a stern man, a Paletine Mennonite, twelve children. If just one spilled food on the table, all twelve got sent to find corners to stand in—facing the wall a good long while.

My momma was raised Mennonite but it never took hold. They would not fight in wars, and my daddy did, and so Momma had to leave home so she could marry him—in Daddy's Baptist church in Birchardville. Old Willie was raised Mennonite and he married his kind, but had fooled and gotten sent off shunned. I figured it might now be my turn to have to leave home.

"Old Willie? Has living shunned . . . been a terrible thing?"

Behind me something dropped onto the porch and I turned to look: Old Willie's pipe lay on the floor at his shoeless feet. He bit his lower lip an instant, staring at me; and when he spoke, it was through his teeth: "Hellish torment," said Old Willie. "Chunks of my life vanished—the gristle and bone holding me together, the farm that bound me to this earth. They cast me out to where wind and cold became my coat and blanket. This heart," he added, with rising voice, "became a pebble!" He slammed his chest hard. "Living is eye for eye, tooth for tooth—and ye ought to learn it young!"

I stood up, walked over, and touched Old Willie's shoulder bone. I told him I was sorry I'd ever asked about shunning. When he came standing onto his feet, I snatched up the cob pipe and held it out for him to take. I admitted aloud the fear worrying me: one more dead chicken and I might could land wrenched from home and punished much like him, thrown out and all.

"How come this chicken killing is going on now, Old Willie? Just when my daddy's gone?" I heard the whine in my voice.

"Don't try to figure out things so deeply," Old Willie answered, sharply. "Ye risk growing up crazy, 'cause ye can't fully fathom the whys of ways without getting frustrated. Angry. Mean."

Light seemed to be draining out of Old Willie's eyes. They began to look wooden. I backed up a step, alarmed.

"Jest look for *pattern,*" he continued. "That's the lesson I'd like ye to learn. The strong steal from them that be weak!"

"Heck but I'm no weakling," I blurted out, backing up instinctively as if his hands intended to grab my neck.

But suddenly Old Willie's face slackened. His bunched-up brows sank back to normal. Speckles of light came into his eyes.

"Ye ain't?" he asked, merrylike, like I was foolin'.

"Surely not," I replied. I hooked my thumbs into my suspenders, and shoved until I let the straps fly snap back against my ribs—which Daddy did sometimes in his moments of huff, if he wanted facts to stand out and get heard.

A cat's grin stole over Willie's mouth. I looked past him, to a white birch gleaming in the afternoon light. *Sun was about three o'clock,* I gathered. Time I got going.

I told Willie I needed to get home right away: get at the garden work, get at the stove wood, tend to the chickens, eat supper—that I was truly hungry. Besides, I said, I had a plan figured out: a way to stop the bear.

"Ye come inside, eat here a minute," Old Willie said, right away clapping me on the shoulders.

Inside his cabin it seemed dark as a cave. When Willie pointed to a propped-up stone, saying it had fossils, I made out only the stone itself. His stove and its upright pipe, I saw pretty well—set in a corner. A wood table and bench. In our house we had a corner cupboard, sofa, two rocking chairs, an old piano, electricity—Old Willie had none of those things.

"Ye sit down," he said, nodding at the bench. On the table was a candle stub that set in the crevice of a flat little rock.

"Nice place, Old Willie," I said, then sat. He grunted

and lifted a dipper from a pail, poured water into a bowl on a shelf, rinsed his hands, and dried them on his pants.

He scooped something from a stove skillet, dropped it into a wooden plate, brought it to me: gravy, goopy gravy with meat and some round bones—cold. "What is it, Old Willie?"

"Crow."

I chewed a bite—the dark taste of dirt, earthy as a gizzard—whilst he brought in the cask, set himself near the door. I swallowed it. Stalling at eating more, I asked whether he knew the relative getting buried in LeRaysville. He stopped his whittling knife and looked at me queerly.

"Yea," he said, "right well."

"How so?"

I soon wished I hadn't wondered: he sighed, and cast the floor a lengthy, gloomy look.

"I guess I better scoot, Old Willie."

"Best ye do," he answered, whispery.

"It's good crow," I stood saying. "How did you catch this crow?"

"Gun."

I strained looking until I spotted it: long, dark, polelike across upturned deer hooves, with a hanging pouch of shells.

"That sure would help in the coop," I said, "but Daddy won't let me shoot. We daresn't have guns at our place. Momma don't allow it, since it's against religion. Little Ben's miracle—"

"Bah! Bah!" exploded Old Willie in a mean fit, shouting onto his feet and towering over me, hollering. "Ye momma stole the farm! Ya! Ya!" He glared at me, thundering, "My wife was barren! I could have no children! So . . . so . . ." He spit onto the floor.

In his hands were the knife and the sharp-pointed stick. I started circling around him for the door. He turned following me, sputtering and stitching up a story: He had need of a new wife, found her, then Elders, my uncle Schaeffer among them, shunned him, forcing him away. His farm fell fallow. "Bah! Bah!" raged Willie. "Ye can't comprehend their cruelty against me!"

When I dashed headlong for the porch he came right behind me. I leaped off and kept running, saw over my shoulder how he was shouting from the cinder block, arms flailing the air: "Too late! too late now! she's dead!"

I ran for the crack of light over the stone wall at the tree line and field. I jumped down into the tall, concealing hay grass and stumbled toward home. Halfways across the field, I stopped as I had to vomit up the gravy and crow. I knelt onto a swatch of bird's-foot trefoil. When I quit, and had rested a moment, fragments of history of the farm—which my ancestors cleared in 1810—came to mind: names of those who'd upkept this land, and finally of Willie—who hadn't. But my own history—with the coop—was mostly the one I gave mind to: me not wanting to be proven a weakling, nor again sent away to Uncle Schaeffer's. Not that the dead chickens weren't a fact, but that I would withstand it and fight against the killing creature with all my strength—prove myself out to be a good protector. I vowed to myself that even little Ben someday—if I ever had to—I would preserve him from harm. And I swore that my plan ahead would work, finally ending all the killing.

Smoke: no creature I knew of came near it. Sun broiling my head and back, I kept on digging a trench to go clear around the coop. Pick and shovel, sometimes the iron bar, for big rock—rock about the size of Pennsylvania. My mind had set on a lot of green wood smoldering in the trench, on stinky, gray smoke after I had added dry horse dung: a slow-burning smelly trough encircling the coop which would be safe in the middle—detached as an island.

When my arms ached I said, "Tough, too bad." A boy growing into a man doesn't sit down from aches and cramps: he hurt if he had to. With the sun slipping down, an evening breeze started up, goose-bumping my sweaty skin so I shivered, and still an acre to go, it seemed. I just plowed on, blisters or no—didn't give a whistle about bleeding hands.

What I did was sing aloud to imagined melodies of our tinny-tin piano. "I've been wor-kin' on-na chic-kin coop . . . all a live-long day." Invented as best I could some of those verses about Dinah: "Dinah won'cha burn, Dinah won'cha burn, Dinah won'cha burn that bear-air-air?" Weasels and all the others. Still at it when dusk came, when Dinah had burned up everything, hundreds of times.

Weared down, I went for the well, brought up the bucket, dunked my face deep into it, over my head—liked to drown. I opened my mouth and let grit wash out, felt coolness stab into my gums, breathed water into my nose to flush it. I lastly hefted up the bucket and turned it over me, shocking the heat which had been sapping my body. Then I filled the feed pail at the shed, called the chickens in. They followed for the coop.

I couldn't help but wonder why the killing creature took such trouble for the coop when fat spring pullets slept in the pines around the old outhouse. Old Willie would probably have said nothing touched them because the watchful cockerels were too dang ferocious. Which would've been right.

Made some sense. But Old Willie seemed half-crazy to me now—a rooster which had turned into a brooder, then crowed from atop a stone egg: Too late now, she's dead!

With the feeder trays filled and all the birds in, I latched the coop door and went for wood: fresh-cut brush the township left alongside the road where our lane juts in—sumac and what not, that Daddy calls "trash wood." I dragged branches trip after trip, up to the trench, rolling them on in; finished the last few yards of digging just as darkness fell. A hazy moon appeared. I filled and hauled baskets of dung and dumped them; got the can of lawn-mower gas kept outside the shed.

Lit it: *whoosh!*—a ring of terrible flames around the coop. Looking up at the orange, faceless moon, I stamped my foot hard and sweared: "Dang weasel, dang bear, dang coon, dang porcupine, dang fox, dang rat, dang snake, dang crow . . . now c'mon here, you just try for one more chicken! ha!" The chickens clucked frenzied inside the coop. I called out, "Your sor-row is over!" and I lay on my back, listening to the sighing sapling wood.

Little Ben was weak because he'd had scarlet fever. What he held, he dropped. He was dead and came back: "God's gift," Momma said, for her newfound prayers of Scripture. Uncle Schaeffer agreed with Momma; Daddy, too. I guessed I did, though Momma hadn't gone much to church until Little Ben was sick, red as a Christmas bow. The doctor said he'd die.

Ben lost all his hair. His white crown looked like an eggshell—smooth and fragile. Bluest veins branched out, ankle to brain. He cried a lot—my ghostly brother—in bed.

The cows had done it—unhealthy milk. Daddy had a

truck come and our herd went off: scolded out the lane, lowing away.

I stayed at Uncle Schaeffer's as Ben was dying. Uncle Schaeffer was the preacher at LeRaysville, but I saw he had guns in his house—against religion, if Momma was right. Uncle Schaeffer's three boys had guns, too. They came home with spring gobblers one day and I saw it: each boy had a gun. Momma perhaps mistook religion, saying it don't allow guns. Old Willie grew up Mennonite; I saw he has a gun.

Protect him, oh Lord. Yes, do. Guard our angel-boy Ben: this was the prayer I prayed as I rose amid the smoke, the dew, and started for the house for bed.

I heard faintly some squawks from the coop, sat up in bed, listened: not chickens—a light rain, falling on leaves, the house roof and the metal one of the shed. *Dang,* I thought, *my fire.* And lay down, to sleep, head under pillow.

Sunrise. "Up sleepy-head," I said, "go look." I got dressed, then ate a raw egg; too hungry to boil it.

I didn't hurry, but firstly wandered to the shed—no reason—then went across to the garden, stood awhile in tomato plants, mostly green-fruited yet. Eventually I went moseying the path, telling my heart to quit beating so hard. At the trench, the wood was cold, wet, and charry—not but few ashes. I leaped it and went on to the coop.

The latch hook still was down in its U-bolt on the door frame: so far so good. Then I pulled the door open, losing all my breath at once: *three* hens torn apart, dumped leafy upon the floor—and a wide-open trapdoor. "Bear!" I shouted. "The bear's back!" The seven remaining hens whisked their heads up and flew in a cyclone out the coop, whirling past the cock bird who was streaking away.

"Old Willie? You Inside? It's me, Tommy." A red squirrel in the beech started up, chattering busybodied. "Go on get out," I said. "Shoo!" A stone missed and he kept on gossiping, informing the whole forest I was there.

I mounted the porch—"Willie?"—but he wasn't at home. Went straight for the gun, took it down, felt it—like a jewel.

Sniffed it. I liked the strange steely oil smell. I hefted the gun to feel its weight and balance. When I aimed it at the door I said, "Blam, you rotten killer bear." Took two shells from the pouch and put them in my overalls. And went home hardly seeing nature—thistles, poison ivy, spiked loosestrife along the wall.

I tried to learn it in the yard: Remington .20, a slit in the side, the wooden stock under the barrel, the trigger. But I didn't much know about guns, and so, after a short while, I walked to the store to ask how to load it right.

It was Bertha who was sitting behind the counter. She had her gray hair parked with bobby pins.

"I'm going to shoot a bear," I said.

"You are?" she asked, smiling at me.

"Yes, truly I am. I'm going to use this gun. Can you show me how to load it?" I laid it on the counter.

"Lord!" she said, jumping up. "Turn that thing around; don't point it at me."

I turned it around so it pointed my way. "How's that?" I asked her.

"Well, did I hear you say it's not loaded?"

"Well, I don't know if it is or not, exactly. I have two

shells in my pocket and I have pulled the trigger a few times. And it has not gone off."

Bertha stared peculiar at me then. Suddenly she was shouting, "Kenny! Come here quick! Kenny!" Her husband came rushing in from his backroom into the garage, with a claw hammer.

I explained all over again.

"Whose gun is it, Tommy?" asked Kenny then.

"Old Willie's. I borrowed it."

"Say you're going to do what again?" asked Bertha, like she'd forgotten.

"Shoot bear," I said for the third time. "One that's killing all my chickens. He just might next be after my little brother."

"A bear's killing your chickens? How do you know a bear's killing your chickens?" Kenny asked, quizzing me.

"I saw it, face to face: a great big black bear."

"Oh? Now, just where did you—" Bertha started.

"Heck, never mind," I said frustrated, cutting her off. I pulled out a shell. "I'll figure it out myself."

"Where's your folks at?" asked Kenny, as I picked up the gun.

"A funeral at LeRaysville, Kenny." I tried poking the shell into the side slit. "It goes here, don't it," I said.

Kenny jumped. "Now, hold on!" he said, sharply. I looked up. 'That's backwards." Kenny looked at Bertha, who suddenly looked unwell, nearly white. "C'mon," he told me. "Outside."

We went up back to his beehives and stood and practiced sighting on them. Over and over Kenny warned me to use the gun's safety. I got fairly good working the gun: slipping a shell in, pumping it out; the spread stance, the trick of folding my cheekbone on the stock—breathing out while pulling the trigger. Expect a kick, Kenny said, and a loud report. After the lesson we went into the store and I bought two orange Creamsicles for the walk home. Bertha kept herself pursed and silent.

Weeded the garden in the late afternoon: cabbages, brussels, snap beans, potatoes. Tied back the tomatoes, pinched off the suckers. For breaks I went to the gun and pretended: *blam!* Sundown, for a swim in the creek, the gun along to shoot bear if I saw him; but had no such luck.

Came back, ate: cheese and apple again—not allowing myself any more of Momma's eggs from the icebox.

Twilight I took feed to the coop and called in the birds: *chick-chick-chick-chick*. . . . I poured out some meal, and then checked that the stone eggs were in the nests, as the brooders often would knock them out in daytime.

The gun and the shells were in the house; firstly I drank two cups of cold water before heading back to the coop.

I crawled in through the trapdoor, closing it after me. Hens looked still to be all right, and the cock bird was on his roof peg. I slid a shell into the gun and pumped it up into the barrel; hunched myself down in a corner. The safety! I clicked it on, then scolded myself for having nuzzled the barrel on my foot.

I was sitting, had even fallen asleep once, when I sensed it was coming, across the sticks and embers in the trench. I could visualize the moon's orange blank orb, the dark sky, a crouching bear, and I slowly stood up—all parts of me seeming to quietly unfold.

It crawled under and bumped against the floorboard. I slipped the safety off and in the oily black light I aimed for the trapdoor, anxious for him to show his head.

A long, dark arm pushed up the trapdoor. The heavy

lid fell backwards silently, no thudding—it was laid down. Then a head and one shoulder rose up in the hole. I saw it was Old Willie, but I was already pulling the trigger.

Old Willie's whittling knife unfolds or I can refold its blade and carry the knife in my pocket. Right this minute, it is open. I am sitting on the well and whittling a stick. I am waiting for Daddy and Momma and Little Ben to show up. Barn swallows are swooping the field. Some minutes ago a sparrow took after a red-tailed hawk, pecking it hard.

I couldn't prevent my finger from pulling the trigger. I was all tensed up, then it was too late. The hard kick drove me off my feet, clear into the wall. I went down shocked. The chickens went crazed, whipping around in the coop. I soon started shaking, trembling, sobbing: I was sorry I shot him.

Old Willie is in the house and I have him in the bathtub covered with water and Epsom salts and some of Momma's canning salt, to preserve him for his funeral. His chest is blown clear through. I have closed his eyes and a stone egg sets on each one.

If I get shunned, I guess I might go live in Old Willie's cabin. Take along with me his knife, the pipe, and the gun. And if I see that dang bear, I'm surely going to blast him apart. For he is here about somewheres. One day, he'll spy weak Little Ben and try to snatch him off to his cave, to pare Ben into slices the likes of these shavings here. I'll stop him, though. Surely I will.

RAMON C. BAUTISTA

The Capture

The Constabulary had finally tracked him down
at the local brothel—
Abundio Espera, the communist NPA* leader who had
killed
more prominent people than any other outlaw
in the history of the island of Mindoro:
Don Tiburcio, the wealthy ricemill owner
found stabbed with a crowbar one morning in his
warehouse
after he refused to give twenty sacks of rice
to the rebels;
En Chong, the Chinese merchant,
hanged from the bamboo rafters of his seaside hut,
his mouth stuffed with his underwear,
when he failed to deliver
ten boxes of canned sardines.

The Constabulary were always amazed at how
bullets seemed to bounce off his body,
like *calamondin*** fruits thudding on the ground,
during nights of shoot-outs.
But the rookies attributed his magic
to a charm he wore between his legs—
a jade pendant (rumored to have been stolen

from the grave of the great Chinese pirate Lim-ah-Hong)
which enabled him to slip from the hands of the law
like a wet mudfish.

But not tonight.
By the blood-soaked bed on which he lies naked,
the barriofolk take turns congratulating Epifania,
the young whore who had divested him of his charm
while they made love.
They examine the jewel as if it were the face of a baby.
How the men gape at and curse his body,
now transformed into a human sieve
by the M-16-wielding soldiers
who had promptly responded
to the pimp's tip.
How the women gasp at the sight of his large member,
still stiff on his belly, as his blood
slowly drips through the slats of the bamboo bed.

* NPA: New People's Army, underground rebel army in the Philippines

***calamondin:* spicy little lemons found in the Philippines

ADAM WOODFILL

Viewmaster

"So whadd'ya think?" Andy said as he walked out the backdoor and onto the deck. "C'mon now, this is the best thing that could've happened to this old house—I bet we're increasing the property value by thousands."

Sarah shifted her position on the green-and-white reclining high-back patio chair and reached for his hand. "It's wonderful, honey, you've really outdone yourself."

"Just you wait 'til I put in the fountain and the exotic fish pond."

"It's really something, I don't know how you pulled it off."

"Careful planning and hard work, that's how, and it paid off . . . we'll have it all—everyone will want to come over just to relax on our incredible deck, that's for sure."

"Well, I don't want the neighbors over here all the time, but maybe once in a while for a barbecue."

He sat down on one of the wire mesh benches near the bonsai garden. "Are you kidding me? I want to show this miracle addition to anyone and everyone who wants to see it. I'm even thinking of charging admission, and lemme tell ya, the people will be glad to pay it."

"OK, OK, Andy—what'll we charge?"

He studied the deck inch by inch, carefully soaking in the fine craftsmanship of his work; the knotty-pine-paneled floor with steps to the site of the future spring-fed pond, the soft glow from the elevator annunciator bulbs in the hanging light fixture above the fully functional bar, the walkway that connected with the circular, enclosed Jacuzzi room, supported by stone columns and surrounded by a variety of tropical hanging orchids, the French doors leading into the house, and the cast-iron trellis being devoured by towering sunflowers. "Sarah, I don't know what we should charge exactly, but I do know that this is the single greatest accomplishment of my life."

She took off her sunglasses and knelt down in front of him. "It is a beautiful deck Andy, but to say it's the defining accomplishment of your life is going a bit far, don't you think? I mean, you did have help in the building, it's not like you hammered in every nail yourself."

"Oh, I see what you're getting at and maybe you're right about the actual construction aspect, but I'm talking about the big picture here, the dream becoming reality. I'm talking about the blueprints and the dirt, not just the wood."

"Andy—we have a thirty-year-old, three-bedroom ranch in a middle-class surburb, and you have drained our savings and run up our credit cards so you can come out here and pretend you're someone else." She walked toward the bar. "Don't get me wrong, honey, I love you to death, but the deck is taking over the house—I think it just may be too much."

"So you think I've lost my mind, do you? Well, correct me if I'm wrong, but aren't you about to open the refrigerator to pour yourself another glass of lemonade without having to go inside to the kitchen?"

"Yes, I was going to pour myself a drink, but—"

"*A-ha!* The mere fact that you can do that proves my

point. Y'see Sarah, the exact spot where you are now standing used to be nothing more than a patch of dead grass, and now look at it, just look down at your feet."

"I told you, it's a great deck, I just don't understand why you're defining your existence with a very expensive home repair project."

"Home repair project? Is that what you think all of this is, home repair? Take a walk around the neighborhood sometime and look at what people are living in these days. You're not seeming to grasp the brilliance and beauty of our niche in the world. Understand, we now live in The House to drive past, even though only part of the deck can be seen from the street. News like this travels fast, I bet people start coming up through the woods to take pictures."

"Shouldn't we put up a fence then, to keep the spectators out?"

"That just gave me an idea. We should install those coin-operated binoculars, y'know, like the ones at Niagara Falls, and that way we'll turn out a profit and no one will actually have to touch the deck."

"And where will we put these things?"

"We'll build them into the fence somehow. That was smart thinking, Sarah, I knew when I married you, you had a good head on your shoulders."

"Well thank you, Andy, it's good to know there were reasons other than love."

"Aw come on now, you know what I mean, you're a good woman that can appreciate and understand fine art when you see it."

"Now the deck is fine art, huh?"

"Of course it is—it's not like it's as simple as a toaster oven, there's function as well as genius at work here."

"And don't forget emotion."

"Exactly—all art has a certain degree of energy within it, and that energy was put there by the person who crafted it."

"But what if the art drew too much emotion from its creator?"

"What do you mean?"

"What if the piece drained the artist, leaving him so enamored with what he has created that he cannot create again?"

"I don't think that's possible, do you?"

"Maybe—why don't we go inside, have some wine, and talk about something else?"

"There's no need, the bar's fully stocked."

MARK JARED ZUFELT

Terezin

children
with their tender, little hands
beat on skins stretched across empty barrels

"rat-a-tat-tat"
cries of anger and confusion
bellow and crash against the mountains

and all the while
calluses are formed on and around
the hard heart
to protect from the beatings
to protect the beat

creation
must mature and advance
to defeat the destruction
so beats are layered upon beatings
and paints are layered upon paintings
while walls of words are meant
to reach for the sky

Elevator

what about
four little
boys running
in cubes
like ants
marching
to a
lemming
mass suicide
for corporate
drop-outs
stressed and
noses runny

like it should be

th h h h h h h
s h e e e e e e
t h h h   h h h
s h a a a a
th   th th th
sha   sha   sha
tha   sha
w h e e
tha   sha
w h e e z e

SUSAN F. BENNETT

evacuating wapello

i dream the FloodMan the night before he comes, i dream him beautiful.

because mollie won't go to the Mississippi and so because the Mississippi had to come to mollie—because mollie won't leave her house that had been her grandmother's and then her mother's and so comes the Mississippi to mollie, because of that we call the FloodMan from kansas.

* * *

you weren't there that summer when the Mississippi crested so high—not the first time once upon a time in june last tuesday—but this last summer year, this summer year it leaps straight up over its banks and lands crouching on its haunches, almost batting iowa all the way to the pacific ocean so that mollie's brother larry who lives in spencer almost wakes up one morning in san francisco and almost spends the rest of his days staring out the window waiting for autumn to come. And it would have happened, too, if it wasn't for mollie and the FloodMan. was that the summer when it rained and rained, you say? and i say yes, that was the summer when it rained and rains. at first the whole state is kaleidescope-clean, all color and shine. the trees are so green, the sky so blue, the barns so red that we spend most of our days canceling visits to the eye doctor. But after the third month everything starts to slip, just a little, to sag under the weight of that water. One day of rain can be beautiful. Three months brings nothing but sadness and a kind of bone-popping lonely feeling, even if you have a family and a dog.

spring in iowa is magic time—like a cow with her cud, Winter has chewed up all the life in the land and spits it back utterly green and transformed. It is magic time and fleeting like magic—it lasts about a week. And then, early june, real early, maybe it is late may, there are three days of Summer—hot, hot—the thermometer, greasy with sweat, slips past 90, 92, 96, 99, and, reaching for the record books, fails with honor and holds for approximately twenty-five minutes at 101. Folks next door turn on their air conditioner. The rest of us take off our shirts and start to work. i get mom's tomatoes in and she sets her . . . i don't know . . . some kind of little feathery flower in the heavy black topsoil. The farmers start planting. The ground smells sharp.

and then the rain starts. at first it is good. my daddy himself is so happy, 'cuz he is one for loving to watch the rain. my mom worries about her glads yet she says it's a grand rain nonetheless. but mollie just shakes her head and mutters something about the River.

but of course the rain doesn't stop. it rains and rains so so much that my daddy by that front room window, his eyes glued to the rain, stares until his eyes get so big we have to take him over to mollie's and mollie has him sit in her back pantry with no windows. his mouth full of cotton, he crouches in the dark while the family paces the outside hall reading *Life on the Mississippi* so's he'll start giving more of a damn about water that's already here, and not worry so much about the stuff not born yet. And it works, too, because when he gets out of that room his eyes are all normal-sized again.

that's how it all starts, because it is after that dad starts going to stare at the Mississippi on the weekends. so one weekend we pile in the rain in the car and we drive through the rain and the constant rain to the cliffs that overlook the Mississippi River near burlington.

it is mom that first notices how high the water seems to be getting. oh judas priest, she says, will you look at that River. and my father says too high. too damn high. and we all very quietly get back in the car. mom has her jaws clenched shut so she can't cry, and i hold my half-empty, unwanted mr. pibb in my hands all the way home, 'cuz we both know all it will take is for someone to spit and the Mississippi will flood. and no one wants to get the blame. renegade River, we think to ourselves. but we're not *so* angry yet. or so scared.

when we get home the tv is on and mollie is there, listening to the anchorman listening to the weathercaster who says rain, more rain. he has a pinched, frightened look on his face and i know then that he can't stop the rain, that no one can stop this rain and the Mississippi is drinking all it can drink and still is too thirsty. swollen, the weatherman says. and he keeps saying how sorry he is. twenty-three feet and rising. twenty-three feet from the River bottom. almost five of me, standing on my own shoulders and all you'd be able to see would be the top of my head and then only for a second because the River is rising.

what about the crops, mom is crying. oh god what about the livestock, the houses, the people. mollie says that she'd heard the folks in marion are blaming the rain on ray debrower the antique man who buys for 300 dollars an african rain mask and the day after he brings it home it starts to rain. and mollie says the people of marion are fools to think ray debrower has any control over anything, let alone the elements and forget about the Mississippi River. ray debrower's dog, she says, barks twenty-four hours a day—do you really think that man can bend anything to his will? and dad says ray's dog is a spayed beagle, and not even jesus, who'd spent all his time with lepers and dead people and bankers and vultures, kept company with beagles. and mollie allows as how that theory is supported in the gospels but says she still doesn't think the rain has anything to do with ray debrower.

the River rises. a month or maybe it was a year later mollie's brother tom is walking his brittany spaniel lucy by mollie's one day and hears her screaming. he finds her hanging off her dining-room table, drying a damp spot on the floor with a hair dryer. she says she can feel the Mississippi lapping at her ankles. mollie hates things that lap—kittens with milk, fast cars in a race, the ocean at the beach. even mollie, who, in her youth, made love once to the Mississippi and had a child with tawny eyes and a heart way too big for her tiny body—even mollie is beginning to hate the River. or maybe she is just scared. mollie says, where do all the children go? where do all the children go? and dad says nothing and stares a little while at the rain. it says on the television that the weatherman's been murdered. and we don't dare cry because the River is so high, but we don't figure it is the weatherman's fault about the rain,

because the River is coming for mollie, to love her and hate her that bore his child, because mollie and the River are somehow *family,* because since that baby was born and died, everyone knows someday the Mississippi will rise and never stop, to mourn its own child in its own way. that's why it's not the weatherman's fault, and i know it, and now so do you.

and mollie's brother tom comes in and says to mollie that her basement's starting to fill, and she'd better come and get her peach pickles up to the kitchen 'fore they float away and mollie's brother tom won't have any peach pickles to eat with cottage cheese on thanksgiving. and mollie and tom go on home with lucy trailing behind, her liver-spotted tail half in half out of the water already beginning to pool in the sidewalks. tom's mustache is white as a ghost and mollie's knees are shaking.

this is the way mollie's house looks. it was her grandmother's and then her mother's. and it's tiny, with shelves in the basement and a washer/dryer set that's so old that the spin cycle makes a noise like john philip sousa and not like the beatles. that house will stand forever, said the man who built it. it'll stand forever, good lord willing and the creek don't rise. there's an attic too, one of those tiny cramped ones with slanted ceilings and tiny tiny windows. and it is filled with the flotsam and jetsam of one hundred years. the sun slithers in in the morning, slowly taking the light with it as he goes over the house. hours later he shines in the back window and a different set of three lifetimes of memories grows warm and starts to fade.

the River is rising as i'm telling you this. time may stop but not the River.

the first floor is right there when you come in the front door from the cracked sidewalk, up the front steps through the door with the stag etched in the frosted glass, through the front porch with the foldout bed and the bookcases. the smell is pipe tobacco, it is strong cold coffee and palmolive dishwashing soap and old house and only mollie's house smells like that. there is a couch underneath the window looking into the house from the front porch. you can look around now. a huge glass container filled with half-dollars or maybe whole silver dollars. the dining-room table that stretches straight back to england and shines faintly reddish. this long dresser thing, it goes along the whole wall, and in it are bowls of buttons and the heavy family silver and the letters from that boy—our boy—that fought in the civil war and who got caught by the confederates and who wrote cheery letters to his mother from the camp and neither the word fear nor the word hate appears among them.

you are in the living room and there is an air vent with a crafty easter egg still hidden inside it. and the best of all things, in between the cabinet and the wall are kept the most best of the best of all things, the coloring books. someone has colored a rodeo pony black—the outer and inner lines thickly covered with black crayon, the body of the horse gently colored in, so that the artificial construction leaps straight out at you and the soft flesh inside seems paler and less real in comparison. someone else colored it, and not you. but now that you've seen it you can color this way for the rest of your life.

in the kitchen is the mouth of the palmolive, but less tobacco, the source of strong cold coffee, always the same old house scent. fudge on the stove, orange tabby, upstairs are two bedrooms and a bathroom which smells like some flower like lavender or something.

that is mollie's house, to where the FloodMan comes.

if you are mollie this house was owned by your grandmother, then your mother, then you. and you will have given it to your daughter, had she inherited your heart and not the River's. sons are born because it happens that way sometimes, but daughters are born to protect their mother's home. in my mother's home the stern georgian facade mutters soft prayers over and over to protect me from harm, three layers of brick, thick carpets and walnut tables lemon-scented all cluster together to keep the rain forever and away from me.

and my mother is there at her home and my father, but mollie's mother is dead and her basement isn't feeling too well either.

and the River is rising. the chief of police's son frank comes and knocks at our door and says that somesuch agency says we've to pack our bags and evacuate wapello . . . and with him is a man in a suit who says by the beginning of next week the Mississippi will wash over wapello and cover it with its cold strong coffee spirit but he says Wah-*pell*-oh instead of *Wop*-a-low and so i shut the door in his face. but daddy opens it and mom cries and daddy holds my hand very tight and when the men leave we start to pack all our things.

things are neither good nor bad, says mother, they are merely ours and that is all. we pack great-grandma's quilt and the waterford bowl and the tables and the books and the pictures and we put them in a truck and we drive them to a safe place and we leave them there and we drive back to mollie's to help her load up her house.

only mollie isn't packed. she's not done packing, she's not even begun. and she isn't going to, either, she says, and mollie's brother tom and mom look at one another and frown.

* * *

look out there, mollie, says dad. look at that. comes the Mississippi, mollie. the River is coming, and we owe it enough that the least we can do is to get out of its way. but mollie just shakes her head.

it takes three days. not to convince mollie to budge but for the rest of us to realize she isn't going to. i didn't realize mollie's brother tom knew that many cuss words, let alone that he knew how to move them around in a sentence, so that sometimes they are verbs, sometimes nouns, sometimes adjectives or adverbs, and once even in a once-in-a-lifetime flash of inspiration, as an entire conjunctive clause.

and mollie just keeps shaking her head and the Mississippi just keeps rising. she's waiting for the River, mom says, and my brother timmy says, she's too old to have any more babies. mollie shakes her head.

and that's when dad decided to call the FloodMan to come from kansas. FloodMan can stop a flood, FloodMan can bring the waters down, not me, not me, only the FloodMan, said the weatherman as he lay dying and everyone heard him, 'cuz they killed him on the air. and so dad calls the FloodMan and he isn't going to come, not at first, but when dad says it is for mollie the FloodMan drops everything and gets on the greyhound express to dubuque. 'cuz mollie alone among all women had been blessed, if only for a minute, with a Child of the River itself.

and we sit with mollie all night while she waits for the River and we for the FloodMan.

* * *

and the bus he rides in on is empty, no living soul wants to tempt fate. FloodMan even has to drive the bus by himself, seeing as how burkhardt, the scheduled driver, knows that he'll make it just fine to iowa, 'cuz the waters will recede back just like they did for the israelites to get to the promised land (although burkhardt wouldn't have called iowa the promised land, seeing as how he's from kansas) but burkhardt knows he'll never make it back to kansas without the FloodMan and sheer fear keeps him from any attempt at bravery.

which is what we are doing, attempting bravery while comes the FloodMan driving the greyhound bus like a bat outta' hell from the western border of kansas to the eastern border of iowa before dad can hang up the phone. FloodMan had help, dad says, someone or something helped him here and mom said maybe, but he'll need all the help he can get to stop the Mississippi now, now that the River has the bit between its teeth, now that the River is entering the quick trip on the edge of town, nosing along its shelves, wet arms encircling the bottled water, knocking it to the floor, setting it free. Join me, whispers the River and the spring water leaps at the chance.

and the Mississippi flows down main street toward mollie's house. and we sit on the porch watching the left road for the FloodMan and the right for the River. and i am crying and my tears roll off my cheeks and down the right road to join the Mississippi as she comes.

when the Mississippi sees the FloodMan he/she/it stops, rears back on its haunches. The FloodMan doesn't seem to notice—he waves hello to the River, marches right up the front walk to mollie on her swing on her front front porch. and the FloodMan puts his hand on her shoulder and says mollie mollie i can't stop this River. nothing can stop this River. it needs to flood the same way you and i need to hate and love—to know it is alive. do you understand? the price will be too high, says the FloodMan. too damn high, says the FloodMan.

the FloodMan has a red starburst on his forehead, and his neck tilts somewhere to the left and down. where's my son timmy, mom says, where's my brother timmy, i echo, but mollie says he's inside and the FloodMan frowns, and he opens his mouth but dad yells the River's gone! the River's gone! and we all look and the Mississippi has vanished. And we sing a little and try to clap the FloodMan on the back and shake his hands but he shrugs us off, his face white. his lips are moving but no words come out. upstairs we hear the breaking of old glass and down from the open window float tiny iridescent pieces of carnival glass that mollie's mother collected and mom begins to scream as the Mississippi River follows the glass like a waterfall, spilling out the open window. shines in the tawny waterfall the memories of mollie's attic, the pictures and christmas decorations and toys, and, finally, like flotsam and jetsam, comes timmy and a baby cradle.

the River, daughter of mollie, father of her child, has come, like a daughter to her mother's house, like a husband to his wife, like father come to see where his daughter breathed once, and no more. the River settles in mollie's house, pushes in the back door, fills the rooms with love and hate and water, and, finding timmy where the baby should have been, pushes him out the window along with memories and broken dreams.

and mollie jumps up when she hears the River call her and opens the door and walks in, and the River makes a clear path to her favorite chair for her and then closes slowly around her and the front door bangs shut and there we are, staring at the FloodMan, and then timmy moans and dad and mom run to him and because he is almost twenty-five he gets up to meet them and he isn't really hurt at all. and the FloodMan says look, timmy is smiling, and he is. and so mom and dad and i smile.

and then dad says get this River out of here. take that River by the hand and walk it home. walk it to hell for all i care.

and the FloodMan says there's a price to pay. there's a price to pay do you understand? and dad says tell me, and the FloodMan says i will take the river away—away for permanent, away forever. if you ask me to take the Mississippi away i will take it far away and it will never run its banks again. and the Missouri, the Great Muddy herself, undulating her way from somewhere up north to meet the Father of the Rivers, even the Missouri herself will wait underneath the arch in st. louis, wait for her man who will never come. all this time she never knew—he loves someone else. but love or no love the River will not return to here, where he loves her that sits in her old chair. and all you have to do is to tell it to go and never return. while i walk the river away you curse it with all the life in your body and you tell it to never return. and dad looks at mom and she at him and both at mollie and then at our house and they say yes, we will say that to the River.

and the FloodMan starts to sing and the River obeys like a dog who wants differently but doesn't know how to fight the hand that feeds it. and the river begins to follow the FloodMan home, to wherever his home is, somewhere far and away.

and the FloodMan starts to leave wapello and he turns to my father and he says curse the River now.

and my father opens his mouth to curse the River but no words come out.

cityman asks us, as we watch our past and our present and probably our future soaked to the soul with the River's spirit, why we don't just move. Because the Mississippi is our home and we are its home and that makes us family. i don't suppose living and dying are all they're cracked up to be, but tell me have you ever seen the Mississippi? it is The River, damn you, maybe the first River ever, the furrow of its bed plowed into the land by the finger of god. and it is every inch The River. my father closes his mouth and he can't drive the River away. and my father says i'm sorry FloodMan. the price is too high. too damn high.

mollie sitting in her yellow chair bends down to the River and she whispers into the eddies and the currents, and the River swirls around her ankles for a moment, and stops flowing. the River is motionless for a fraction of a second. and then slowly begins to flow again.

* * *

and the FloodMan says if you don't mind i'll walk the River home to its banks now, like i first promised you, for i am a man who must keep at least one of my promises, just as i am a man who must punish those who cannot keep one of theirs. and he doesn't wait for an answer, just crooks his arm and begins to sing and from out of the house a delicate finger of water twines around his elbow and the River eases underneath the casements of mollie's house and lifts it right off the foundation. and mollie sits in the front window, holding her memories and waving good-bye, good-bye, as she smiles and we realize she is going home with her man to her child.

and still the FloodMan sings and sings his song, and i find myself falling and following, the water kissing my feet and the warmth and the love and the hate and the Flood taking me with it, taking me home to live where the Mississippi lives, to go home to its banks, its bends, its crests which rise to meet the banks which rise to meet the cliffs which rise to meet the sky. I am going home to its tiny islands, its soft warm silt, which trickles down to the water table which soaks all the way down to the center of the earth. i am blending with its tawny soul.

gently and quietly through the empty streets of wapello walks the Water the FloodMan mollie and me. all night and into the day we walk as my parents' screams fade into the distance. i walk in a dream until the River lies down with mollie and mollie's house and the FloodMan and me, deep in her bed, loveless and hateless now. and slowly wind we our way to the Missouri and the sea while a jar of peach pickles and the agonized cries of a mother and a father float through the empty streets of wapello.

kicking and screaming
    we were married
kicking and screaming
    we made love
kicking and screaming
    we bore children
kicking and screaming
    we raised them
and sent them off
into the world kicking
                    and screaming

Flirt

nimble,
you
thrust,
and queried

clumsy,
I
dodged,
and fainted

TERRY ENDRES

Rabbit at the Bat

"C'mon, Rabbit, now," Mac bellowed from third base. "I smell some clutch! Bring me in, now."

It wasn't bad enough to be two outs in the hole in the bottom of the seventh inning; I had to have my own booster section standing on third.

"Gimme some base knock, now!"

So it all came to me. If I could break the ten-ten tie, the Steamroller Blues' season continued. And me, I was just a slap hitter. No real threat to go deep. Not that it mattered with two outs and our slowest runner on third.

Now, don't get me wrong. Mac Bessler was a solid first baseman, but he wasn't much help when he hit the ball on the ground. He was lucky the Jumpin' Jacks' third baseman's throw sailed wide of first base and into the stands, allowing Mac to reach second. Luckier still was that he was the leadoff hitter for that inning, and Bill Carson's slow grounder to the second baseman moved Mac to third. An infield fly by Larry Wills ensured that I could be the hero . . . or the goat.

Up until then, I'd had a pretty good day: a walk, couple of line drive singles to right field, an RBI, and a run scored. But it's always easier to concentrate when there are innings left to be played. If I choked, we'd have to face extra innings and the top of the Jumpin' Jacks' lineup. Their first four hitters had produced eight of their ten runs.

"C'mon, Rabbit, only a run away, now," Mac reminded me enthusiastically.

Waving my bat in short arcs, I stepped into the batter's box and looked out at the field. The right fielder still hadn't caught on to my opposite field approach. Good.

The Jumpin' Jacks' pitcher looked as big as a dumpster as he swung his arm back, then forth, then let the ball go. It fell an inch short of the plate.

"Ball!" the umpire spat.

"Good eye, Rabbit, good eye!" Mac chimed in.

Rabbit. A high school nickname that recognized my one atheletic asset: speed. Unfortunately, with all the Jumpin' Jacks playing in and Mac at third, a ground ball hit wouldn't quite work . . . my speed wouldn't count.

Once again the pitcher drew his arm back in a short swing and lofted the ball toward home.

"Strike!"

"C'mon, Rabbit. You got two more. Make 'em count, now."

It was a habit of mine to wait for the first called strike before I'd start hacking. If the next pitch looked as good as that one, I'd have to give it a whack.

Stepping out of the batter's box, I looked the field over again. The right fielder still hadn't moved from his straight-away spot. Fine. I'd gotten good at masking my stance so that the defense could not anticipate where I would take the ball.

Slowly the Jumpin' Jacks' pitcher wound his arm forward and floated the ball toward me. I could see the seams weren't spinning. If I hit the thing just right, I could tail it down the line and away from the right fielder.

Quickly, I shifted my feet and brought the bat around in a downward arc. There's no way to really describe a well-hit ball. It feels like the bat slices right through it; there's almost no vibration along the barrel.

Like a madman I scrambled down to first. I could see the ball cut toward the foul line, the panicked expression on the right fielder's face as he dashed to his left.

As I raced toward second I saw Mac trotting back to third. He held his hands out about six inches apart. The ball had landed just foul.

Disappointment washed through me. Now I had two strikes. I had to keep the next hit fair.

Picking up my bat I climbed into the batter's box. A quick glance around revealed that the right fielder, in fact the whole team, had shifted two steps toward right field. Great, I was forced to pull the ball.

I'm sure it was psychological, but I never experienced much comfort pulling the ball. I felt like I had to lunge too much to make contact. Usually, if I pulled the ball, I'd pop it up or shoot a one-hopper at the pitcher.

"C'mon, Rabbit. Shake it off, now!" Mac cheered me on.

"You're one and two, batter. Keep it between the lines," came the umpire's wisdom.

Once again the pitcher brought the ball plateward. God, it seemed to take a long time getting there. Again, I could see there was no spin on the orb. He was actually inviting me to go to right!

Sluggishly, the ball topped its arc and slid toward me. It was going to be a bit inside, and that would make it difficult to take to right. Nevertheless, I slid my left foot toward right field and . . . jerked the bat around in a sharp circuit.

In anticipation, infielders and outfielders jumped two

steps farther to right field. Bad move. I'd chopped the ball to the left side of the infield and then went flying down to first. The shortstop was almost standing on second base when he tried to reverse his motion, but he found a soft spot in the infield and landed on his back.

The third baseman had pulled so far in that even though he was moving in the right direction, the ball skittered past him before he could get his glove down.

I hit first a step before Mac touched the plate with the winning run.

The ball stopped rolling about three feet into the left field grass.

DONNA H. MURPHY

Baby

Baby had a secret
hers alone to tell
she locked it in a seashell
and dropped it down a well

maybe not a bright girl
she wasn't stupid either
and knew just where to hide
when papa came to meet her

what was so gently whispered
to that seashell fine and frail
would make the coldest killer
blanch a deathly pale

it's safe there in the water
and no one needs to know
that there is more to Baby
than Baby cares to show

The Dream

here's a simple thing
a few digits and a ring
when beneath it silence sings
in bright colors for the master

here, the hiding place
within a fine bone vase
that knows nothing of grace
but a thin veneer of laughter

that's where it stands alone
child with a stone
where darkness overgrown
will sate its tainted hunger

eyes closed, you're free to go
dancing in the snow
safe from every blow
a dream that's dreamed of slumber

King Lear: "Blow, winds, and crack your cheeks! rage! blow!"

KOURTNEY HARPER

Terzanelle

I've made an adjustment, an automobile,
a window that runs through the world.
Now I'm fast as a roach at the top of a wheel.

I was slow as a stone now I'm hurled
through a crystal, a glacier, a small town of ice,
through a window that runs through the world.

Your world is a movie and I've come to splice:
all clacks and bright light but no sound
in a crystal, a glacier, a small town of ice,

in a cube where I am in bounds,
an electron in motion revolving in ice,
a small clack, a bright light, but no sound.

But I'm fast. I have passed you by twice.
As the slow that you talk to stand still
an electron in motion revolves by in ice.

I surpass all the slow by an act of my will.
I've made an adjustment, an automobile.
And the slow that you talk to are all standing still.
And I'm fast as a roach at the top of a wheel.

BRENN JONES

In Search of David Byrne

Some have his dark hair, others his slender frame—though he may have gained weight during his thirties and probably would look surprisingly short in public, as rock stars and famous actors inevitably do. This East Village café with mustard and burgundy walls is a second home to eccentric middle-aged men who appear tattered and worn like the couches they sit in. While he too is eccentric, I am sure that his problems are much different from theirs. In my mind, the ones that resemble him are the hungry college students. But tonight I would be just as likely to see my lover, who is studying across the sea in Scotland, as I would be to see him. No, he is not here, nor was he in front of Tower Records when I passed by early this evening. I did not see him at the corner of Allen and Houston as I left my apartment tonight, and he did not seem to be at Luaka Bop on West Twelfth this afternoon, though he may have been behind the library stacks or hiding upstairs.

New York City is full of famous people, and full of people who look like famous people. I thought I saw Brad Pitt walking toward the Angelika Theater last week. It was probably just somebody striving for his look in order to get dates. Two weeks after moving to the city, my friend Scott and I went to a Bleecker Street bar called The Bitter End. Noah, a guy I had just met from work, was playing there with his band. He mentioned that Natalie Merchant might show up to watch him perform. Noah did not *seem* like the lying type, but he did have several other unbelievable stories, and when I'd first arrived in New York I was suspicious of people and their stories. We got there early and immediately saw Noah in his red Texas Rangers baseball cap, but when we scanned the room we could not spot Natalie Merchant.

Our disappointment ended abruptly. As I was returning from the bathroom another subject of Noah's stories passed right in front of me. Sitting across from us, just three tables down the room, was Uma Thurman. "Quick, go get some cigarettes, she's starting to smoke and we need to look cool," said Scott. As we smoked Uma appeared to be looking at us. She was no doubt looking for somebody behind us. Scott was so encouraged by her glances that the following day he asked his girlfriend if he could hook up with Uma, should the opportunity present itself.

We walked home through the cool autumn night, passing through patches of New York City odor that have little to do with any season. While Scott was blathering about Uma, I was quietly buzzing from my first ever cigarette. A few days later I talked to a friend of a friend who spotted David Byrne in front of the Tower Records on Fourth and Broadway. She said that Byrne was staring at something in the window. She remembered that he had sideburns and was wearing a blue beret, but she didn't notice what he was staring at. She didn't approach him and say hello, or ask him any questions. She didn't care. I was devastated to miss him again. I had been missing him my entire life. But maybe if I were there at the right time he would come again.

Two days after Byrne was at Tower Records, I called my lover across the sea. My friend Ammitai, who also needed to make a call, headed outside to find a pay phone. Just as Ammitai left the building, David Byrne stopped his garage sale bicycle with flat handlebars at the corner of Allen and Houston, right in front of my apartment.

When I was in fifth grade I always went to George Shuffelton's house after school. We were at the age when your best friend is also the person you hate most and spend all of your time with. In his kitchen we invented a game called Oafkie, which involved whapping a little puck made from newspaper and Scotch tape with Oafkie sticks, also made from newspaper and Scotch tape. The kitchen was small so we ended up pounding each other into the corners and cupboards a lot, sometimes getting in play fights or real fights—it was tough to tell. When we were done the sun would divide us with a sharp shadow across his oak kitchen table. We would eat pear halves and George would wander off to the living room and play some Mose Allison, whose voice sounded like the pear halves tasted. On other days we drank Cokes in white plastic New England Patriot cups and listened to an album by a band named Talking Heads. The first song was "Psycho Killer." I took notice.

I bought every Talking Heads album and a tape of their concert film. I was entranced by Byrne's carved eyes and the tight contours of his face and neck that were accentuated when the stage was lit from below. A simple tan suit gave his body more edges. When dancing Byrne resembled a Paul Klee painting in motion. His head, arms, and shoulders continually flailed back as if being shocked by an electric fence.

I learned that Byrne, like me, was born in Scotland and taken to the United States at an early age. I imitated his dancing (though it seemed more natural to me than imitation) during the ninth-grade homecoming, and plastered pictures of him all over a self-imagery collage for health class.

Though you may disagree I insist I have never had a crush on David Byrne. I have crushes on people I see as separate from me—people who possess a personality, style, or appearance I do not have. But with myself and Byrne there is no such distance.

"David Byrne, right?" "Why yes," he said. They shook hands. "Wow, I can't believe this. I really love your work and . . . and my friend upstairs is going to kill me for meeting you. He's such a huge fan of yours and he lives right in that building there, but he seems to be having a hard conversation with his girlfriend in Scotland." "Oh," said Byrne, and then—in a soft stilted voice both mocking and compassionate, "Boo Hoo."

When Ammitai returned I was still on the phone. When I hung up he told me his unbelievable story. I laughed, and then began to march through the loneliest months of my life.

But missing David Byrne like that was not all bad. While I missed him I could hear his voice clearly. I know how he said it—first up "Boo" then down "Hoo." Like a lyric from one of his songs—ironic and layered. I knew that he and I both understood that. Furthermore, Byrne thought of me, so now I had an excuse to write him more than simply a generic fan letter.

In my letter I told Byrne my friend had met him at the corner of Allen and Houston. I did not mention that I was the one upstairs. He may have figured that out. I asked him if he would like to meet me for coffee or lunch. I painted navy-blue bars around the perimeter and sketched little houses in watercolor pencils next to my name. I knew he would get back to me, because I spoke directly of our bond:

> When I first moved to the City several months ago, I imagined seeing you somewhere. I realized that if by coincidence our paths did cross, I would not know what to say. Then I saw *Talking Heads vs. Television* at Lincoln Center, and while exiting the movie theater I knew that if I saw you I would tell you how much I loved the film. At the end of the film you said (I do not recall the exact words, but I understood the meaning) that you hoped at some point during the concert, if only for thirty seconds or a minute and a half, that the band and the audience would lose all sense of time—they would experience something transcendent.
>
> This happened to me repeatedly as I sat cramped in my seat with the huge speakers overhead. I felt as though I were under a breaking wave that was thrusting me to shore. One scene kept playing over and over in my mind. It was during Once in a Lifetime, when you juxtapose the clips of natives in religious trances with the music and your own imitative dancing. I imagined how the people felt—the people whose bodies chattered uncontrollably like teeth after a swim in the ocean. I imagine they were both sinking and lighter than air. I had felt like that once in my own life.

His address was a P.O. box at Cooper Station, so I stuck a James Dean stamp on the envelope and gave it to the teller in the Cooper Station Post Office. Over the next few weeks, I made sure to wake up when the mail was delivered at 11 A.M. When anybody called the phone rang with possibilities.

But every morning the mailbox was empty and when the phone did ring, it was not my lover either. I distracted myself by sorting my belongings, which lay scattered in various piles on my bedroom floor.

At night I lay alone attacked by my mind: *Doesn't he understand how I am suffering? Have my emotions deceived me? What happened to our connection? Who the hell is he?* Then, finally, *When is this going to end!?*—and back again, *Doesn't he understand . . .*

The note under the buzzer read, RING BELL AND TURN KNOB so I was optimistic that I would get in. It was not the first time I had been to Luaka Bop, Byrne's recording label and the place where he works. From the outside it looks more like a residence than an office, with a stoop and a black front door, big windows, and black shutters. I had previously been content just to peer through those windows. I had seen the familiar albums high on the wall, and paced back and forth on the sidewalk to get a better view. That had been enough for a while.

"Who is it?" The woman had a British accent and her voice came clearly from the intercom. Startled, I rifled through possible answers before finally, after a few seconds, stating my name. The buzzer sounded. With feigned confidence I strode through the front door and took a right through a second glass door inside. I stared blankly at a woman on the phone, and in the corner of my eye I noticed another woman approaching from the side. I turned to her, then darted glances behind her, where the space was divided by three library stacks.

"Can I help you?" she asked. She was only my age, and probably didn't even like his music, but no doubt she worked with him every day. She just stood there in front of me, waiting for me to say something. I stuttered. I was going to ask her whether David Byrne reads his fan mail, and then I was going to ask if I could see him, but her skeptical expression prevented me from proving my connection. I finally inquired whether David Byrne was going to be in concert anytime soon, and hoped that her response would give me an opening. She shook her head with a slow and mocking gaze, and when I shut the black door behind me I knew I could never return.

So I heard that they've put my name on their list—people who like David Byrne a little too much. They may even have a mug shot, though if they looked at it closely, I am sure that they would see him in me. In my isolation I fear my sanity is slipping away. But don't you see that I am not dangerous? Don't you see that I am not a threat to you, and if you could understand, I am less dangerous to me? I am going back now, not to Allen and Houston, but back across the ocean to the country where he and I were born. I am going back to where he lived before ever recording an album and where I lived before ever hearing his voice. There, the calm sea at night is patient from waiting.

ELIZABETH HANSEN

How to Start a Band

The true dream of every American teenager is to be in a band. Getting paid to make noise and party. What could be better? As a former member of a band and an avid concertgoer, I consider myself an expert on rock bands. Here are some easy suggestions to follow when starting a band, whether you have talent or not.

The first thing you need to decide before starting a band is the type of music you are going to play. I suggest trying to sound like the popular alternative/rock band Pearl Jam. Their music is loud enough that it is not necessary to be proficient with instruments, but not so loud that it turns off female listeners. Since most bands are Pearl Jam rip-off bands, you need to find a way to distinguish yourselves from others. Unnatural hair colors, weird clothing, multiple tattoos, Halloween costumes, and playing drunk are some ideas. Experimenting with the last one might even improve the sound of your band.

The most important part of your band is its members. Three people is the minimum needed for a rock band. Remember the fewer people in your band the fewer ways you have to split your earnings. In a three-member setup, the positions needed are a guitarist/vocalist, bass player/vocalist, and a drummer. If no one in your band has any musical experience there are some basic guidelines to follow. First, the ugliest person gets to be the drummer. There are no exceptions to this rule. If you want people to come and watch your band even though you have no talent, you are going to have to rely on looks. Hide the ugliest person behind the drums. Very few bands have good-looking drummers, but for some strange reason even fewer bands have ugly bass players. The best-looking person in your band should play bass. The person remaining should play guitar. The lead vocalist should be the better singer of the bass player and the guitar player. If they are both equally awful, then the bass player, being the best looking, should sing.

Now you need to think of a name for your band. I suggest a two-syllable name. Pearl Jam, Green Day, and No Doubt are all two-syllable names of successful bands. Anything over three syllables is a band-naming don't. I bet you've never heard of Treacherous Jaywalkers, the Geraldine Fibbers, or When People Were Shorter and Lived Near Water.

Acquiring equipment and transportation are the next steps in starting your band. Buy the ugliest amps and instruments you can find. This will reduce the chance of people trying to steal your equipment and also help to distinguish you from other bands. Ugly is also a good idea for your transportation. A big ugly van is the only way to travel. Keep your van free of bumper stickers advertising your band or any other. Instead invest in bumper stickers from the NRA and AM-band country music stations, and make sure to get one that says, MY KID BEAT UP YOUR HONOR ROLL STUDENT. These stickers will keep thieves from thinking your van is loaded with expensive equipment and, hopefully, appeal to the police officers that pull you over when you're speeding to your gigs.

Songwriting will be perhaps the hardest part of making your band work. Your songs need to be fairly short to keep the attention of your audience. The language in your songs needs to be somewhat clean. Obscene enough to appeal to rebellious adolescents but clean enough for radio play and purchase by minors. Make the lyrics to your songs confusing and hard to understand. The most critically acclaimed albums are the ones in which the lyrics make absolutely no sense.

The most expensive part of promoting your band will be cutting your demo. Find a phone book, look up recording studios, and call around for the cheapest rate available. On your demo, I suggest two of your own songs and two of another band's songs, covers. Do one as closely as you can to the original song and one as far out as possible. This will prove that you can possibly be an entertaining cover band but that you can also improvise. *Do not cover a Pearl Jam song.* I know I told you to sound like them, but never admit to it.

Now mail those demos out to area clubs and record labels. Be sure to include a biography and a picture of the band. The picture doesn't actually have to be of your band. However, try to include at least one member. That way when you show up for a gig you can say that the other people were kicked out and replaced by former members of The Dependents or whatever fake band name pops into your head.

If you follow these tips carefully, you may someday live the rock 'n' roll lifestyle you have been dreaming of. Good luck!

RUSTY BARNES

Special Rider Blues

for Polly Jean Harvey

Some lounge singer crap connoisseur
Tom Waits version of classic thirties
tear in the beer song, the fog machine
spitting up into the crowd and everyone
moving in some slow sort of rhythm, mostly
their feet, from the waist up they don't
do much but grind, and the guitar squealing
almost, like a demonic guinea pig and in
the middle of this this woman.
In black, but not black which is what you
might expect in a blues bar some 44DD
special rider in a low-cut red dress flounces
on the shoulders maybe, but this was not her.
Instead this skinny white girl crushed velvet
skirt dress thing with leather boots, thigh
high dominatrix glossy leather and no chest,
cigarette in the hand while she held the mike
stand like it was a cock, fingers down,
caressing from the bottom and this voice
full-throated, no Janis scratch 'n' roll

but a deep contralto cigarette voice,
a long-haired voice with a curl, tendrils
dropping over and into your face,
some topping sex flush sweat, but

that she would sing you to sleep in a
bath of street-lamp light, pull your hair
in her smoking fingers to the back of your
hackled neck and through, and that she,
and you and he and everyone who hears
is thinking their own transport thought
to deal with curling under an afghan alone
and taking a secret self in hand,
masturbating the blues away,
she is one on the stage, your thoughts
are collective, with the fog and the notes
of her quaver-rich witness-bearing vocal ululation
and you suspect that somehow she has what you do not,
synchronicity, harmony, an astral acoustic kink
partnered with the souls of the black-strobed room,
some greener self within you expands, lysergic acid
mainline immediacy, no screams after the 125th hit,
a synapse misfired neural blurt of god moving through
her into the crowd, god—humanity—being—
psychic reality kick, and then the note is gone,
swallowed in her slim throat, blessed illusion washed away
a thin-sheeted wall of blowing dioxide cigarette
smoking trails of orange coals tossed away, ground
into the dirty concrete floor, under the heels of the world.

IRENE POLEMIS

White Bundles

Dad called the trip the only alternative. But I thought from the beginning that it wasn't an alternative at all, leaving for the island in the winter. Lindos was barren in the winter. I remember those trips, those times when it wasn't a holiday. Out on the deck of the boat I was cold. Those blankets left on the benches were damp. I'd sneak down and find empty cabins, but Dad would spit at the ground next to me when I asked him why we couldn't go in. He'd curse and become dry toward me. So I'd curl down near him and try to stay out of his way. When the boat reached the harbor I'd watch the people below, some had cars on board. The guard at the narrow staircase on our level would move away and we'd go down and out. My father said there never was a cab for us, although there was a row of them. One time I rode on a donkey. But most of the time we walked.

Dad said it wasn't a long walk, that a man needed to fill that space between his chest and back with good air, that his feet needed to walk hard on the earth. He'd stamp his shoes and dance. I looked at the valley of olive trees below, then up along the dry mountainside. The goats watched, but the small shepherds never noticed anything. I did like the way the sun rose slowly behind us. It warmed me. Maybe Dad was right. Maybe the trip wasn't long. When we reached our village it was still early morning.

I hated to walk in the alleys Dad found, knock on the wooden doors, and wait for someone to answer. It seemed that no one ever knocked on those doors without being invited. I don't think we were invited. We never went inside, waiting always at the door for Dad to finish talking. I hated the way Dad mumbled, "Piraeus doesn't have work for me, the heating bill, and my Anna has grown old for a young woman. Two daughters. If I can't feed them I won't need to worry about marrying them off. The boy's still a boy. Look at him. I'm making him grow as fast as I can. We'll put him to work soon. But that Piraeus. There's no work. I'll send him to sea soon. He could work for your Captain Nick. He could clean for him and cook for him and do everything our young sailors do. But he's still a boy. His arms are too thin."

Captain Niko and Captain Georgios and Captain Eustasios. The names just changed. And I stood there feeling naked and wishing I were younger. And wishing that Dad would just go to work when they called him and stay at one job long enough.

Mom liked to be simple. She burned incense in the house and put fresh flowers in front of the icon of the Virgin Mary and prayed, her voice strong and sweet and everything felt good. Even Dad wouldn't yell except when I went near her when she prayed. Like the time I tried to lift the red glass of our candle to light the wick and Dad heard the glass clink and took me outside and whipped me hard with his belt. It happened very fast. I didn't understand it. In fact when I think about it something shifts in my head like a bone with worn cartilage. I don't remember each of my father's whippings exactly. Just my confusion. The waiting between each one. And Dad saying, "Religion is for girls," in a shaky voice.

Ever since then I went before the icons only when Dad was out, never touching anything in case he remembered where things were. On Sundays I could hear the deep sound of church bells from the basement where Dad made me scale fish and I prayed silently and tried to remember the feeling of Mom burning incense at home.

Coming to Piraeus from those trips to Lindos Dad was happy. Old Miss Olga gave him a bottle of Metaxa each time along with a thin white envelope, which he folded into his pocket with whatever else he gathered. We sat on the floor near a wall and he drank from the bottle. Some men up there with us were looking at Dad and the bottle and Dad knew it. I pretended I didn't see them. When Dad put the bottle to my mouth I tried to refuse but he'd pinch my arms hard. The juice choked me and burned my throat and I felt my eyes water and redden. I drank it trying not to look at anyone.

Now we were going with Mom and Jean and Little Metaxia and it would be terrible. I thought we could keep these trips between Dad and me and all those villagers and that somehow the begging wouldn't come back with us, the embarrassment wouldn't be too well known to my mother and sisters. So that they could walk throughout the village with some self-respect and wouldn't know what those stares really meant. I never wanted little Metaxia to know anything other than Daddy is back from Lindos. Let's see what he brought us this time. In fact, I thought until fairly recently when Dad started taking me with him to Lindos that I wasn't too different from captains' sons, that I was even luckier because my dad was home and their fathers were gone for months.

It was true. Soldiers were everywhere. We stopped going to school a few months ago. Mom stopped going to the market. We stayed in the house, with the curtains drawn, and went to bed early because we couldn't keep any lights on. Somehow it made my stomach feel better. I don't think I understand this fully, but there was no food in the house. Mom and Dad looked like they were expecting some soon from somewhere. When I asked Mama for something to eat she didn't say anything. I believed things had to go back to the way they were.

But Dad said there was no alternative. There, in Lindos, we could at least breathe and walk outside and try to live through the war. I couldn't imagine this at all. Everyone would know us there. But the plans were made. I heard Dad late at night. Stavros, the man who was always at the café with Dad, was going to use his boat. Something about soldiers by the docks at night and parties, laughter, and women and that we'd be able to get into the boat and sail quietly at first until we got out and when he'd use the *motori.* I didn't want to hear about it. Breaking the curfew so that Dad and Stavros could have some kind of fun. How could he with Mom and the girls? I didn't know what my father was doing. I opened my door and saw him sitting over the kitchen table, his arms resting heavily on the laced tablecloth, his red hand tightly holding a small glass. Mama was there. I thought Stavros had come in. But it was Mama rocking and nodding her head slowly. Little Metaxia close up against her. I didn't understand. My mother was in on these plans too? I must have gotten something wrong. Half the time things didn't fit right in my mind.

I went back to my bed and let my body rest. I could feel myself getting heavier on the mattress. Mama was in this too. It was OK to let them take care of things. It felt good to think like this. I could feel my stomach crank. I had a strange feeling of a movement outside very different from our lives inside. It was like going under water and looking at the small fish swimming slowly near the bottom.

I thought my mother was a soldier when I woke up. She stood upright and firm next to my bed and looked down at me with a man's face.

"Get up. Here, take this and follow and listen carefully."

She handed me a white bundle tied in a knot. It was light. I wore the clothes she pointed to and the slippers and followed closely behind her. At my bedroom door I had a vague feeling that I should look back, but there wasn't any time. There were more bundles at the front door. Jean was standing there waiting. She looked older. She looked like a woman.

Dad was at the table folding gold coins into handkerchiefs. He bunched the folded package on his hand, showing it to Mama. She nodded slowly and watched him hide it in his shirt. It was important I knew where that package was.

The street was dark. We walked closely together. Mama held little Metaxia tightly to her chest. I wondered if the baby could breathe. We walked fast, really fast, and we were so close I felt as if we were walking in circles. Dad pointed to the next street which could be seen between houses. I had a glimpse of men lined up and walking slowly. But a house blocked my view. We stopped at the passage where the house ended. Dad looked in their direction. Then we went. I saw the line of men again. One of them was looking at us. But the next house blocked my view. I didn't know whether or not I should tell Dad. I squirmed up to him. I felt it was my fault that the man saw us. At the next passage we stopped again. Dad peeked. I grabbed his pants. He turned at me abruptly and pulled me hard by my shirt. I looked at the passage expecting my whole family to be shot. And all due to me because that man saw me and I didn't tell Dad.

The man in line was looking at us again. This time Dad saw him. He threw up his arm and waved. His white hand opened. It was large. The man put his head down and continued to walk. The next house blocked our view. And by the next passage we had crossed the street and walked into a dark alley that led to the sea.

Everything happened quickly after that. It was very dark and the sound of ripples in the water was scaring me. Somebody whispered and we went toward him. I didn't know if we should go toward the sound or run away. How did Dad know? I followed closely behind. At this point I had no choice. Things happened very quickly. We were in the small boat. I knew it was Stavros when he came up close. His face was big and his breath hot. I think Dad and Stavros were smiling after that.

When the boat started to drift out I felt unsure, unsafe. The earth was no longer under my feet. Although my family was near me I felt as if we weren't close at all. I wanted to cry but I saw Jean's outline across from me. She sat quietly. So I kept it in. It was hard in my chest. The swish of the oars, the push, the cold breeze. These made my eyes lock wide open. I couldn't blink. My eyes were dry. They burned. When little Metaxia started to cry my breath stopped. I thought some soldiers on the docks were looking at us. I could see the outlines of their bodies against the bright lights of the café. Two lifted their rifles. I thought we'd get shot. Dad grabbed the baby from Mama's arms and covered her face with his hand. But she cried louder. My mind isn't working right. He held her like a doll over the side of the boat. The baby's crying was louder. I think he plunged my little sister headfirst into the water. He did. He did. All of us shook. The boat shook. It rocked violently. We didn't speak. We didn't say a word. Just Mama cried. My eyes were locked hard on her. It was very dark, black, and I couldn't see her. Her crying was inside of her somewhere as if she had an apple in her mouth. It was like the sound I heard at Dad's side of the boat in the water. Dad made his way to Stavros, crouching and balancing. No noise came from Jean. I could sense an emptiness. It was as if all our weights floated away in one ball in the sea.

Far out where the lights of the port were small and hazy Stavros started the *motori.* There was something safe about the sound. It drowned away whatever was beyond the boat. Jean got up quickly and sat next to Mama. I wanted to go close to them too. But I couldn't. I thought I ought to have gone to Stavros and Dad, but they sat close to the motor motionless. Stavros steered with the metal bar. There was no work for me there with them. So I sat with my back against the edge and felt the cold mist on my arms and felt somehow that this was all I could do. The stars in the sky were bright. The waves of the sea were full. I felt the boat rise on each wave and stay there for some time until it dropped. I felt myself very far away from everything. I had no idea what we were doing. I wished someone would tell me. Sometimes my heart would beat fast and hard and my hands would sweat and become cold and I would have a sense that Dad didn't know what he was doing. This idea scared me. But somehow Mama's presence made things right. Not that I thought she knew but that she cared.

Something woke me. Maybe it was my nausea or the sun coming up on the horizon. A large deep violet ball. In the boat were our white bundles, and the way everyone was lying crouchingly and awaking slowly I thought I was in a hospital. I imagined everyone had the bitter vomit taste I had in my mouth.

Little Metaxia wasn't with Mama. I hoped she was packed away safely in one of the bundles. But nothing moved from within them. Still she could be sleeping in one of them. I was surprised when I turned around and saw Lindos behind me. The houses along its port were light blue and pink and light green. The colors were playful.

Dad was sitting in the same position I had last seen him in near Stavros. He sat crouched, looking down. His body was angular. He looked old.

The port was inviting. Although I had just awoken I sensed that once we reached it I would sleep. I thought about fresh water.

"We have to hide. We have to go north and go through Gourni where there are fewer people," Dad said.

Stavros looked at the port. He hesitated to respond to my father and I hoped he'd disagree and take us straight into the port that looked warm and friendly to me. I had never seen our village this way. I sat always at the café with my father looking out from it. From here I saw our village spread whole before us. I wasn't tight in some alley, pressing against the walls of someone's home asking for money.

Stavros steered the boat away from the port.

STUART MILLER

Mozart and apples in the afternoon.
Squabble of birds at my window
as the evening nears. I fit them in
to the small cracks between life and life.
Going to work and to sleep.

There are pieces of the day
made for nothing. The landlady's note
left folded in the hallway. Shirts
hung on the verge of weightlessness.
The years would have gone by anyway.

And we even return to these
labors at the proper time. One hears
the harbor one cannot see, and finds
the world pared down to the singular:
A gray hair. A hole in the carpet.

LINDA E. SMIT

The Victors

the body lay there
flesh stripped from the chest
as though the lungs were too warm and wanted air

it didn't move
but the wind blew locks of hair
over frozen, open eyes that stared unseeing

it didn't laugh
but the birds made giggling noises
while they took the eyes from its sockets

it didn't leave
but the worms found paths through flesh
until only the dark-stained grass was left

JOSH NIEMAND

Squids on the Dock

I once saw squids on a pier in Mattapoisett.
They were sucking and popping
and shooting ink across the dock.

I tried to talk to the old man who had caught them.
He just made sucking and popping sounds
and shot his line into the water.

I think he could have told me great stories.

SCOTT NAGELE

What Beggars Can Do

What will I do without him, she thought. *What in the world will I do?* It was a big question in a small world. For more than a year now, her world had consisted of one lonely, characterless room. It was perfectly rectangular, with spotlessly white walls. Why did they always have to be white? Many times she wished she had the strength to fling the tray of mushy food they fed her up against the wall, just to give it some color. It would certainly be worth the missed meal.

Besides the medical accessories that her condition required, there was only her bed and a padded chair alongside for furniture. There was a small closet in the corner, behind a sliding door. In the closet was a dress and some other of her things that she had last worn so very long ago. Of course the dress would be far too large for her now, but she didn't really ever imagine wearing it again. Opposite the door was a small window, with white curtains drawn back, through which she could see only sky. On the wall beyond the foot of her bed, staring her right in the face, with a most peculiar thing: a plain, round clock, complete with second hand—the kind that is bought in quantity for schools or new office buildings.

The clock was the lord of her small world. Her life was ruled by it. They brought her meals when the clock said it was time. They bathed her when the clock gave its permission. They hooked her up to various apparatus, and forced pills down her unwilling throat at the clock's command. It flaunted its power. "Look," it seemed to say, "I have taken another second away from you. Your life is mine to take as I please; and in my own good time, I will take it all. See, another second gone. Or is it a minute? An hour? Look at me. It is most entertaining when you watch me take your time away."

She supposed she could have had the clock taken away, but she had a couple of secret weapons against it. What the clock did not know was that she gave away seconds, minutes, hours, freely. The moment that she would have hoarded had been lost long ago. Then, moments were precious. Now, moments were just empty containers. She would give them away to anyone who had more use of them if she could. But she could not; so she fed them one by one to the hungry clock, and let it think itself all-powerful, to her silent amusement.

Her great ace against the clock, however, was that at every fourteen revolutions of its hour hand, it brought him. Every Tuesday evening at six sharp he would come. Since she was first brought here, he never missed a single Tuesday. Several people came to see her for the first couple of months, but the number of visitors soon dwindled. It was, she knew, a hard chore to make oneself do for very long. It was no pleasure to come here. She couldn't blame them for finding things to keep them away. Yet, he still came, although he, more than the others, probably had better reasons to stay at home. He was the only thing that had anything to do with her life now. He was the only thing that had anything to do with life at all. She would have shoved all the days that weren't Tuesday down the clock's throat, and shortened her life by six-sevenths, if she could only just have all the Tuesdays one after another.

And now it was Tuesday. The clock seemed to be grinning. It was after six; and he hadn't come.

Strange, she hadn't ever felt like she really knew Harry until her husband, Bert, died. They'd had so much fun together—the four of them—all those years ago, when they were young. Bert and Harry had been best friends forever; and through them, she and Harry's wife, Grace, had become just the same. Harry and Grace were such an enviable couple. Harry was always so modest and shy. Grace, on the other hand, was outgoing and playful. It was her playfulness that shone its light on the vast reservoir of humor that was pooled just beneath Harry's stoic facade. Likewise, it was Harry's sophisticated humor that brought out the depth behind Grace's flirtatious cover. He needed a woman who would play to his wit. She could not play to a small-witted man.

Grace got along well with nearly everyone—Bert foremost among them. They acted like old school chums. They were completely at ease together. This was not the case between their respective mates. There had always been a level of awkwardness with Harry. From the very first, she thought the world of him, but she never knew quite what to say to him, when they were together. She could not bring out his wit like Grace or Bert could. It seemed like Harry was afraid that if he relaxed, he would say something that would offend her. Sometimes it seemed like they tried too hard to make each other comfortable when they were alone. In the end, their private conversations rarely went beyond small talk.

But when they were all four together, all awkwardness evaporated. Then, the pressure to make Harry feel it was all right to joke was gone. His wife took care of that. Those were such happy times. Other friends joked that neither couple had children because neither pair would leave the other alone long enough to produce any. The four of them had truly grown old together; and for that unusual fortune, she was grateful. It would have been nice to have had the best-buddy relationship with Harry that Grace had with Bert, but she always knew that he really did feel great warmth for her, even if he couldn't put it into words.

That all changed five years ago when Bert died. Their mutual grief, it seemed, gave them a common ground on which to build. She could see clearly that Harry had made the conscious decision to look after her. Suddenly, thirty years of awkwardness just seemed so damned silly. They began by remembering the funny things about Bert, but they soon realized that they had a lot of things to talk about. After so many years of being friends, they were finally buddies. It was just such a shame that they had spent so long being afraid of each other.

For thirty years she had considered Grace her closest friend, but now it was Harry who was the rock to which she found herself clinging. Grace would always be a wonderful person, but her friendship did not know how to adapt. Harry, however, seemed to sense the new emptinesses that needed something to take up the nothing. Every Saturday afternoon, Harry would come by to see what needed doing around the house, and in her spirit. She wondered when he had time to keep up his own home. Even more, she wondered how lonely she would be without Grace and Harry—especially Harry.

Then, when Grace's health started to fail, of course, she worried about Grace, but she also worried about herself. Naturally, Harry would need to spend his time looking after his wife. That was only right. She could not expect much companionship from him anymore. Yet, she needn't have worried. Harry still found time to fix the sink, and lend an ear. He was stretched thin she could tell. She told him that he didn't have to come so often, and wondered if it sounded sincere. Probably, it didn't. Or maybe it did, but he would have none of it. He kept coming, more and more often unshaved, or in wrinkled clothes, but he kept coming. It was as if he had made some kind of secret pact with her, or himself, or the spirit of Bert, that he would always be there for her. It was clear that the burden he had placed on himself wore heavily, yet he never once said a word to that effect.

In a way, she felt guilty that he spent time with her. Grace was only getting worse, and he had enough to take care of at home. At the same time, she worried that he would stop spending time with her. She valued his friendship like never before. He showed her that someone really cared about her. She needed that. She wanted to lend support to him and Grace, but illness had turned Grace inward. Grace did not wish her friends to see what disease had done to her. Maybe it was best just to send kind words through her husband when he stopped in, as he loyally did, until that day, just over thirteen months—and much more than a hundred years—ago.

She hardly remembered that day. It started out just like every other. She may have felt a little light-headed that morning. She tried to recall if she did. She couldn't. She was fixing lunch. Then there was black. Then fuzz, and blur, voices—distant and frightening—hands—pulling, lifting, hurting her. Then black again. She went through this cycle again and again. Black to fuzz to black. Silence to voices to silence.

Finally, she separated herself from the dream. She became distinct from the lights and the noise. She came back into herself, and reeled in her own identity from the chaos. It was his voice that triggered her self-consciousness. He sat beside the bed, reading the newspaper aloud. "Shlaat krimp trunf eport has no basis in fact, a spokesman for the President said." She could hear his voice clearly now; and she felt safe. She could not speak. She tried to turn her head toward him. It was so heavy. It moved so slowly, but he saw it, above the paper. He nearly needed a doctor himself, from leaping so wildly out of his chair, but he soon dragged one into the room to look at her, and verify that she had returned.

A while later, they brought her here, and this little room became her world. Eventually, she was able to speak very slowly and softly, but it took so much of her strength that she could only stand to say the very simplest things. She had all too few people to speak to anyway. The initial group of well-wishers dwindled week by week. The nurses were overworked, it seemed. They were kind to her, but they had little time to stay with her, always rushing to solve some crisis elsewhere. It was only he who had time for her. Every Tuesday after work, he came. She saved her words for him. Sometimes to say hello, and later, good-bye, was all she could muster. Whatever she found strength to say, it was enough for him. He filled the empty space with his words, and his warmth. He would tell her about what had happened to him at work, or what was happening in China. Other times he would read humorous books to her. He brought her the world—the big and the little—always with a smile and a wink.

The one topic he did not mention much was Grace. Grace's condition was very painful to him. Although he would share all of his laughter, he would not share his pain. Once, several months earlier, she collected her strength and whispered, "How's Grace?" Before he could catch himself, his smile faded. "Oh, well she'll be all right. She just needs some time to rest," was all he said. He quickly picked up the book he had brought and began reading a lighthearted essay to her. She never asked again.

For over a year, it rained six days a week in her world. Only on Tuesdays was there sunshine. They gave her newspapers and magazines, but it was so hard to do anything with her hands that she couldn't read but one page without being overtaxed. No, she got all her news from him. She got everything she valued anymore from him. Everything else was just routine—the same things they did to her every day, to keep her alive until she died. And now was that all that was left—staying alive until she died? It was seven-thirty. Visiting hours were over. He wasn't coming.

There are a lot of seconds in a week. She felt conscious of every one of them. The clock seemed to have discovered that it was actually the slowness of time that bothered her. She tried to occupy her mind with other things, but it always came back to the fact that, for her, there were no other things. Her only diversion was in speculation. Why hadn't he come? Had something happened to him? Was he in an accident—in the hospital—dead? No, must not think like that. Must think positive, like—like what? Like she had finally worn him out? Could he no longer bare to look at that pitiful, barely alive, old woman? She had broken the spirit of all the others so long ago. Had she finally, now, caught up to him? And what if she had—he had lasted over a year. God, what if the roles were reversed? Would she have been able to bear him in such a demoralizing state? Maybe something, an emergency, came up. He just couldn't get here on Tuesday. But he could've come another day. Enough of that. Just leave him alone. He'd done more for her than she could ever ask, or repay. Just pray to God that nothing has happened to him; and be thankful for all of his friendship. What time is it?

At last she cleared all of the myriad seconds away from in front of Monday. Just one more day. And then it hit her—just one more day. For the whole week, time had stood still because, deep in her heart, she had unquestioned confidence that he would come this week. Now that confidence wavered. What if he didn't come this time either? If he didn't come, should she conclude that she had seen the last of him? Maybe not, but she sure couldn't expect him anymore. And what if she couldn't expect him anymore? She'd better start thinking about that. The possibility was only a day away. What would the world be like without him? It'd be exactly like a ceiling and four walls and a clock. In the beginning, God said, "Let there be a ceiling, four walls, and a clock." On the second day, he put her between them all, and called it quits. Harry would come though. He had to. If he didn't come, she would die. She promised herself, if he didn't come, she would die.

He did come. She had not even time to breathe a sigh of relief before she realized that he was different. He seemed exhausted. The smile he normally greeted her with was gone. He looked tentative, eyes aimed at the floor, as if he could not face her. The image he presented struck her as one of the child who broke his mother's antique vase playing ball in the house. Did he feel that guilty about last week? He gently slid the chair up next to her bed. When he had seated himself, he finally raised his eyes to meet hers. Now she knew it wasn't guilt. It was pain—the kind that makes a rock cry.

"I want to tell you why I wasn't here last week," he said. She knew that he wasn't explaining why he hadn't come so much as easing himself into telling her what she now already knew. "Last Monday," he continued, voice fading, "uh, that morning, Grace—ahhh, whhhooo—Grace—she died." The words didn't want to come out; and when they did, they came sideways, causing him to flinch in pain. He put his face in his hands, to hide the tears he could not hold.

Through great effort, she raised her arm, and put her

hand on his forearm. “I’m so sorry,” she whispered with all her might. She took a deep breath. “I loved her too.”

He looked at her over his hands. “I know,” he said, “I know.”

He was silent for a moment. Then he began to talk. She was the only person on earth with whom he could remember Grace so intimately. He recalled all the wonderful qualities about his wife that they both knew so well. As he talked, her face and eyes told him that she too remembered all those things. He talked straight through till it was time to go. Before he left, he actually summoned a brief smile for her.

She went back to approaching Tuesdays with confidence. He did not disappoint her. He came again every Tuesday at six sharp. Their visits were different, however, after Grace died. Before, when he talked to her, he’d say things that were intended to keep her in touch with the outside world. He read her news, and told her stories—all having to do with the present. Now when he spoke, it was of old things. She could see his eyes straining to see into the hazy past. He seemed to lose himself in their younger days. He dredged up old memories that she had nearly forgotten, of her and Bert, and him and Grace. Whereas before he would scarcely mention his wife, now he spoke of Grace at length. He rarely brought anything new to tell her; and she wondered if he paid attention to anything new anymore. It was as if nothing of note could happen, now that Grace was gone. He didn’t smile as much as he used to. In fact, he often brought himself to the point of weeping. But it was clear that there was nothing else about which he wished so much to talk. He began coming to see her on Thursdays as well.

Sometimes she felt hurt that he appeared to be turning over the remainder of his life to the past. She wished he could talk about tomorrow for a little while, instead of only seeing all those yesterdays. It was nice to talk about them sometimes, but he was living on them. She feared that they could not support him. But she went on listening patiently. Maybe he would talk all the old days out, and then be able to move on to the future. She would give him time. She had, after all, little but time to give. If he needed to draw still more tears out of himself, she would let him. Of all the things in the world, he alone gave her something to care about. Being a beggar, she could not be a chooser. She preferred his smile, but she would take his tears, if that's what he chose to share with her.

So it went, he communicating to her through his memory, she answering with the compassion in her eyes. It was thus for several months, until the day that she began to slip back into the darkness from which she had first emerged to this room. They took her to different rooms, where they could better keep watch over her. They moved her to hook her up to machines that they could not bring to her. He followed where he could. Whenever they would let him near, he would speak to her resolutely, as if his will alone would make her hear him. But for all of his emotional energy, she was conscious of very little of what was becoming of her, or of him.

At length, the experts concluded that there was nothing to be done for her. So they brought her back to her room, to live her last in the place she had lived so little for so long. He was with her whenever he was allowed. He spoke to her with more passion than ever, as if he were desperate to force out all the words he had left. Some of his words, she heard. Most were indistinguishable from the swirling dreamworld that filled the bulk of her mind. A few, however, would find her momentarily lucid. For a moment now, and then again, she knew it was him. She recognized the words. They made sense. But she could in no fashion respond, even to the point of letting him know that she heard him. Then, he and the sounds he made, were drawn back into the walls of the vortex, being mixed into the unrecognizable medley that was every dream or memory that still dwelt in the recesses of her dying mind.

In the last of her lucid moments, she heard him plead, "Not you too." For an instant she knew exactly what was happening to her, and to him. She knew the past several months better than she could ever have remembered them. In that instant, a voice—her own voice—echoed through her head. "Beggars can be givers," her voice said; and she smiled with her soul. Then the dream devoured her.

Someone had to come to tell him it was time to go home. He felt her condition better than all their machines could calculate it. Even though the machines showed no immediate danger, he knew there was no point in coming for the next visiting hour. She would not be here. At the door, he took one last look at her. "Good-bye, Marie," he whispered. As he turned to face that dauntingly huge world outside the room, he asked himself, "What will I do without her?"

JOSEPH GONNELLA

from Sir Isaac Newton

Unforecast clouds obscure
A perfectly predictable eclipse.
Steeped in the substance of his dreams
He weighs the evidence of things unseen
To calculate the force of water and to clock,
By Jupiter's missing moons, the insistent beat
Of absolute duration. He hatches from Galileo's
Golden egg a new science of dynamics,
Wrestles Descartes' vortex from the sky,
Tracks the image of his father in the stars
And lays his mother's jeweled crucifix
On the brow of an all-pervasive deity
Whose electric and elastic spirit
Dances to demonstrable laws.

Eternity reveals eternity; infinity blossoms
From infinity. Time is equable though
Nothing made can measure such perfection.
Space is everywhere immovable.
Stillness insists on stillness; motion, on motion.
Action and reaction are equal and opposite.
Each body's changing rate of speed
Is a gauge of implicit, animating force.

Cumulative simplicity destroys a universe.
From these ruins Newton builds his edifice.

Do dancers sway or are they swayed?
Earth and moon, blood relatives, wheel
Around a common center. Movement around
And movement forward are one. *In our world*
Each body embraces every other in proportion
To the product of their masses and inversely
To the square of the distance between their centers.

The calm occurrences of night defeat
The final sapphire light of day. I chart
Newton's voyage across an immeasurable,
Dark abyss, his eyes on lookout
For the fatal star, his fingers spinning
Embodied silhouettes. Ether is the food
Of planets; its density increases from the Sun
To Saturn and beyond. The universe is shaped
By choice and not by chance. A very real angel
Moves within him and a face, like Newton's own,
Stares back from the fire inside the sun.
God is the system wherein all things find their place;
Space, the divine sensorium. Within the dark
Of Newton's cold machine is a womb
To birth new creatures for our dreams.

TODD LAZARUS

Black Ants

You could have died a thousand deaths,
By runaway caboose or wayward launderette,
Milk poisoning at the corner grocery store,
Or a rabies bite from the Chow next door.

Lying on your back, listening to mingling
Black ants debate your impertinence to fate
While headlights flash snapshots of broken
Bones piercing your ankle. It's no surprise

That speeding car that stole your breath and
Crushed your side was your omen to decide,
Whether the proof is in the pudding
Or somewhere way up in the sky.

KRIS R. DAVIS

You Can Go Home Again

So there you are, nude and sprinting across your trailer, hoping to God above that the Nelsons have stopped spying in your windows. You've got twenty minutes to get ready for a date that you forgot you even had. His name is Alec and he's waiting for you at Sesame's.

You fiddle with your hair in the mirror and realize that the only healthy portions left are the brown roots that peek out beneath the white. You haven't seen the sun in months, and your pale skin almost glows. After two or three layers of gooey makeup, you look somewhat healthy.

You keep yourself crouched down under the open window in your bedroom and search for your cleanest dress. It's a black one with a zipper down the back. You run down the hall while both putting on shoes and contorting your body trying to get at the zipper.

The front door to your trailer hangs off its top hinges from where your last boyfriend slammed you into it. You leave it dangling there and rush off to Sesame's.

Sesame's is packed with its regulars, so you push your way through the crowd to find Alec. You hope that you can recognize him. The only things that you can remember about him are his short height, thick mustache, and pointy sideburns. There are at least fifty men in the vicinity that fit the description.

You decide that you'll just sit yourself near the pool table and wait for him to find you. As you look around, you think that you should start hanging out in more respectable places. The floor is coated with a layer of sticky beer. The ceiling is coated with a layer of brown cigarette smoke. The walls are coated with a layer of women just like you.

A man approaches you and you assume that it's Alec. He asks you if you'd like to go home with him and you say yes. Anything to get out of Sesame's. As you are walking out, he asks you if your dates are expensive. You tell him that he'd be surprised at how cheap you are.

He reads you your rights, and you ride down to the police station. As you stand by the phone, you can't think of anyone to call. The only number that you remember is your mother's. She comes to bail you out and is silent in the car. She is driving you to her house.

It is the house where you grew up. Large and white, it stands by the creek that you used to soak your feet in when you needed to think. The house was the envy of the neighborhood. Cars were always stopping to take a look at it. Once, a date of yours drove you up to it and told you that he'd end up in a place like that one day.

The inside is decorated in the Early American style. All of the furniture is covered in plastic. Your mother says that plastic is easier to clean. You suspect that she just doesn't want anyone to feel comfortable.

You go into the kitchen and she fixes coffee. She sets a fresh cup in front of you and starts in on small talk about the latest weather reports. It's almost as if her daughter hadn't spent the evening in a cell with a woman named Candi Flip.

You notice that your mother has wet down a rag and is now wiping off your makeup. You push her hand away and she goes off into her lecture . . .

> You never loved me. . . . If you just believed in the Lord . . . and those awful clothes. . . . I know you want to give me a heart attack. . . . Your brother would never . . . the neighbors will just love this. . . . Don't you ever stop and *think???!!!*

After she stops speaking, all you can hear is the loud ticking of the grandfather clock that stands in the hallway. Your father slides silently into the chair next to you. He smells of cigarettes. His forehead creases as he looks at you. The stress there makes you feel worse than any words your mother could speak. He puts his hand on yours and your mother leaves the room. You can hear her slamming doors and tossing objects around the room above you.

He asks you to come home, but you will only agree to that if your mother moves out. He says that will never happen. He offers you money to move out of the trailer, but you like it there. At least that's what you hear yourself say. He hands you a blank check and stands up. He tells you that your room is ready. You don't have a way home, so you stay. You leave the check on the table and walk upstairs with him.

Your room is exactly how you left it. Shelves full of stuffed toys and awards line the far wall. A pair of roller skates hold the door open. The closet is stuffed with clothes that you haven't seen in years, but could never seem to be able to give away. A corkboard above the bed has photos of young girls smiling and holding their arms around each other. You've changed so much that you nearly don't recognize yourself. There is a nightgown set out for you on your bed. You instantly know that your mother picked it out. It lies there pink and frilly. It makes you sick, but you put it on anyway and try to sleep.

The smell of bacon wakes you up. You can't remember the last time you ate breakfast. Hell, you can't remember the last time you were awake for breakfast. You put on a robe and go downstairs.

Your mother smiles and sets a plate of food in front of you. You finish it in an instant. Later, you spend close to an hour in the shower. You are amazed that the water never turned cold. A trailer shower has to be finished in under four minutes.

In your room, you find that your mother has washed your clothes from last night and that she's neatly placed the blank check on top of them. You put on the dress and leave the check on the bed. As you stand there, you want to forget about what you've done to your life. You want to jump back into the pictures that hang above your bed.

Your father is downstairs reading the newspaper. You ask him to take you home. As always, he does what you say. As you pass your mother, she looks away and continues with her cleaning.

You approach your trailer and are suddenly ashamed. Your father walks in and examines the door. He doesn't say a word. He removes your robe from one of the springs that poke out of the folds in the couch, but still doesn't say a word. You offer him a cup of coffee before you realize that you haven't got any. You search in vain through your empty cupboards.

Your father stands up and you see the tear before he

has a chance to hide it. He walks out to his car and pulls several empty boxes out of the trunk. He walks back in and starts placing your belongings in it. You can't move and he won't stop. You unfold a box and help him. You want to come home.

CINDY DACH

After the Wind

It was the second day that the wind had not slackened. Mary stood in her white dress, sheer from the sun, in the doorway, holding the screen door at bay. She called once, "William," and then stood silent waiting for a response. A second call, "William Jason Connolly," and time passing again. The wind roared a huge rush, a rush larger than the constant momentum, and picked up branches from below a tree. In the air the branches rearranged themselves and settled back down on the walk, a few feet in front of where Mary stood holding the screen door. "I can't," she screamed. "I can't go on fixing everything that's broke. William Jason Connolly, you need to get back home." She released her hold on the door and stepped back into the house, down the hall with the cracked gray tiles and into the yellow kitchen, painted by her husband when he had been home. The wind stirred the man and made him seize up his belongings and go out after it. That's how he had phrased it to Mary. When she had been eighteen and he nineteen she had seen this as romantic, creative, endearing. All words she had used as she embraced his photo into her skin and spun slowly for her mother to see.

ERIN SMITH HILL

Naked

I heard a tiny voice
stripped bare in the darkness
whisper haltingly
toward his deep, even breathing
I need you

I need no one
in the light
never have
my voice well-dressed
in polished layers.

I recognize me
when daylight covers
my hidden places

and my confident cloak
protects me.

I don't know
this small, naked voice
exposed at night
when the enshrouding darkness
reveals me.

Between the Leaves LARRY DECKER

Contributors

Writers

Dan Bentley-Baker was born in New Orleans, but has settled in Florida. After graduating from the University of Miami with a degree in Psychology, he spent twenty years teaching, then retired to write and raise his young son. Having returned to the classroom to teach composition and business writing full-time at the college level, Dan has just finished his second novel, which he hopes to publish next year.

Nigel Assam grew up in Trinidad, and has been living in Yonkers, New York, for the last twelve years (with time out recently for a stint in Portland, Oregon). He holds a B.A. in English Literature from Purchase College. Nigel's work has appeared in the journal *Medicinal Purposes,* and he co-edited an underground 'zine called *Stigmatic.*

Heather Prince received a B.A. in English from Valparaiso University in Indiana. Her poems have been published in *The Lighter,* and in 1994 she was the recipient of an Academy of American Poets prize. Living in Evanston, Illinois, and working in acquisitions for IDG Books, Heather is supporting her husband, Tom, who is in chef school.

Kelly Scott grew up in southern California and graduated from the University of Missouri with a Journalism degree. She lives in Cedar Rapids, Iowa, with her husband, David, and daughter, Andie.

Wally Swist has lived in rural Massachusetts for the last fifteen years. His poems have appeared in *The Anthology of Magazine Verse and Yearbook of American Poetry, Appalachia, Poetry East,* and *Yankee,* among other publications. He has also published a dozen collections of his poems, several in limited editions, from such presses as Adastra Press and Timberline Press. Wally is the recipient of several awards and a grant from the Connecticut Commission on the Arts. His latest full-length book is *The New Life* (Plinth Books, 1998), a collection of his lyric and short narrative poems.

Daniela Heggem has been writing for most of her thirty years. She currently leads a very successful writers' group that she established at the Barnes & Noble store in Long Beach, California. Daniela also has an extensive background in theater—both backstage and onstage. She dedicates her first published poem, "Sense of Sight," to Mark Palermo and Michael Simpson, who have passionately supported her work.

Jerry Monaco is a philosophy student who worked his way through school driving a taxi. He has edited the literary magazine *Chalk Circle,* and published a volume of poetry, *What the Drowned One Dreams and Other Poems.* His short stories have appeared in small magazines. Jerry loves writing movie and book reviews, and is at work on his third unpublished novel.

Linda Brunner writes that "being a resident of planet Earth in the 90s has increased my poetry output along with my need for the silence of trees. I reside in rural Missouri with several."

Lake Boggan was born in Windsor, Colorado. She began writing as a teenager in the turbulent sixties, and has produced poetry, short stories, and nonfiction prose. Her current work is a collection about her father, who fought Jack Dempsey, invented the Silver Jet Weedburner, and gave her the gift of art. Lake lives in Portland, Oregon.

Matthew Kane Markham writes: "My life is a short story without an epiphany. I watched cartoons in the 70s, MTV in the 80s, and started writing in the 90s. Like most booksellers, my love of the written word pushed me into the book business. If you love to read, there's no better career than bookselling." Matthew lives in Jonesboro, Georgia.

Michele Stuart lives in her hometown, Salem, Massachusetts, where she and her spousal equivalent spend far too much time playing with their computers and their cats.

Debra Williams is the author of *Emerging*, a collection of poems. Her work has appeared in several anthologies, including *Beyond the Stars, Inspirations, The Paterson Review Journal,* and *Best Poems of 1997*. She won the Editor's Choice Award in 1996 and 1997 from the National Library of Poetry, as well as the 1996 International Society of Poets Award for Excellence. Debra lives in Manhattan.

Peter McNamara was born in New York City (District #93), raised in New Jersey (District #130), and graduated from college in Philadelphia (District #77). Peter and his wife, Nancy, have a daughter named Keaton, known to all as Kiwi. Currently managing the merchandise at the Barnes & Noble store in Metairie, Louisiana (District #105), Peter observes that this surburb of New Orleans "suspiciously resembles the Garden State that I grew up in 30 years ago, proving that, wherever you go, you can always find a little bit of Jersey."

Judith Martin Straw lives in Venice, California, with her husband, Joe Straw, who is a filmmaker. She grows her own tomatoes and herbs, and has a collection of cookbooks that would make you salivate. Her writing is currently featured in the poetry anthology *Echo 681,* and she is finishing a collection of short stories and working on a novel. This is her first published fiction.

John Barrios has recently moved back to San Francisco. Between moves, he worked in the Barnes & Noble store in Buffalo, New York.

Washington S. McCuistian grew up in Tulsa, Oklahoma, and lives there now. He is a student of Taoism and Buddhism, and has started work on a novel. He also paints.

Anne Hawkins hears music whenever words bump up against each other to form sentences. She currently works as the Community Relations Coordinator for the Barnes & Noble store in Topeka, Kansas. Anne is also an events coordinator at the Kansas History Center and the director of an English handbell choir. In her "spare time," she pursues a Ph.D. in History at the University of Kansas.

Patrick Robbins works at the Barnes & Noble store in Augusta, Maine. A graduate of Colby College, he was taught creative writing by Richard Russo, James Finney Boylan, and Susan Kenney. He has written a screenplay, a young adult novella, and a novel about a suicidal procrastinator.

Patrick is twenty-seven, single, and rumor has it he's never run out on a check.

Lisa Linn Kanae is a graduate student in the Creative Writing Program at the University of Hawai'i at Manoa. In 1998 she received the Academy of American Poets Award at that school. Her work can be found in *Bamboo Ridge: The Hawai'i Writers Quarterly* and *Oiwi: A Native Hawaiian Journal*. If you happen to be strolling through Kapiolani Park at about sundown, you'll probably find Lisa walking her orange dog, Tehani.

Caroline C(orrie) Reich is a freelance writer living in Charlotte, North Carolina. She grew up near Boston and is still a dedicated Bruins fan. She has a bachelor's degree in English from the University of Massachusetts at Amherst. Prior to that, she spent a year at the Benenden School in England, studying literature and art history. Caroline's book reviews have been published in various regional newspapers, and she is, of course, working on her first novel.

Anne Riley is a Barnes & Noble store manager in Lafayette, Indiana, and the single mother of two active teens. As such, she has no business sitting on her front porch, pen in hand, until 2 A.M. every morning, burning through one legal pad after another. But there she sits, scribbling away. "Hazards of the Road" is her first published work.

Rachael Y. Banning is a Florida writer who also does feature reporting for the local St. Augustine newspaper. St. Augustine, Rachael reminds us, is the nation's oldest city. In her spare time she enjoys writing poetry and is currently working on a novel.

Kimberly Greenfield was living in Lincoln, Nebraska, when we last heard from her about a year ago.

George Carner lives in Astoria (Queens), New York. "The Pond" was the first story he wrote, and the first to be published. It is dedicated to Peggy Rambach.

Edric S. Mesmer is pursuing a degree in English at the State University of New York at Geneseo. He has been working at Barnes & Noble since 1994.

Adam Henry Carriere was born on Chicago's South Side during the Kennedy administration. A survivor of twelve years of Catholic schooling, he holds a degree in Film and Video, as well as one in Professional Writing. Adam's ink energy has appeared in *Odyssey* and *QTribe*, and on hundreds of piquant postcards mailed throughout the world. Adam has recently completed his first novel and a collection of poetry drafted in the Ile-de-France and Normandy. He lives in Las Vegas, but dreams in Paris.

Kurt Smith is a retired elementary school principal. He was awarded first place in the Clark College fiction contest for a story titled "Water to the Mountain." In addition to poetry and stories, Kurt has published a puzzle book of mathematical logic. His hobbies include biking, music, chess, golf, cooking, and reading. He lives in Vancouver, Washington.

Jennifer Velasco has been published in *Type* literary magazine and the anthology *Still Waters*. She received a B.A. in English from Southwest Missouri State University and resides in Springfield, Missouri. She believes, to paraphrase

Winnie-the-Pooh, that poetry isn't something you get, it's something that gets you.

Michelle Rieman hails from Rockford, Illinois, and has lived nearly everywhere, but calls Naples, Florida, home (because it doesn't snow there). She has one son, no cats, and an addiction to chocolate.

Mathew Sanborn Smith was "utterly astonished to be born and later became a part-time writer." He lives in Florida with his energetically imbalanced family of four. He hopes to be the savior of the human race, but will keep one foot in retail in case things don't work out.

Alan Walker grew up in Madison, Georgia. He found one outlet for his lifelong love of literature as a book buyer with the Barnes & Noble Merchandise Group. Alan was also an accomplished actor, a designer of paper dolls, and the author of an unfinished play, *Lives of the Saints,* as well as many poems. He dreamed of someday having his written work published. Alan died in New York City in May 1996. His family and friends miss him very much.

Judy Ryan attended the University of Iowa School of Journalism during the sixties. In spite of being bombarded by reality for almost three decades, working as a journalist and corporate communicator, she still believes there's a place in the world for things that are beautiful.

E. A. Gibson has degrees in English and American Studies from Michigan State University. She is currently living in Minnesota, working as a technical writer in the computer industry. She hopes to launch a full-time career as a free-lance writer sometime soon.

Cliff Boyer has a Master's degree in Literature, and has been published in *Scrawl* and *Soundings East*. He and his wife have recently moved to Bend, Oregon, where they are enjoying the great outdoors. Cliff has two dreams: to make a living as a writer and travel the world (not likely), and to live in a cabin on a lake in the woods with his lovely wife (more likely). Until either of these dreams comes to fruition, he'll continue to walk his path—one step at a time.

Teresa Hamann pursued an interesting if not successful career behind the scenes in the Los Angeles film industry. Following that, she returned to her home state of Montana to resume her interrupted college education. A challenging creative writing course inspired her offering in this anthology. Having completed a B.A. degree, Teresa is preparing to enter graduate school.

Arcelis Girmay is a Documentary Studies major at Connecticut College, where she was awarded the Charles B. Palmer Prize from the Academy of American Poets. She writes fiction and nonfiction, as well as poetry. A nonfiction piece, "A Day Like This Outside," about a family living with AIDS, is forthcoming in *Salt* magazine. Arcelis is currently interning with CEDEHCA, a human rights organization in Nicaragua, and working with women and the preservation of their oral histories. She plans to attend graduate school.

Linda Miller-Knowlton was born in California and spent part of her childhood in Ireland. She has been writing since the age of seven. She attended the London School of Economics and worked as a fashion model in the English capital. Linda's work has recently been published in *Music from a Farther Room,* a new literary quarterly from Long Beach City College. She has three sons, and lives in Long Beach, California.

Andrew Rutherfurd hails from Hong Kong. He has written fiction for most of his twenty-six years. He is currently living in San Francisco, working on his first novel and trying to find the perfect time of day to write.

Timothy Juhl lives in Dunedin, Florida. His work has appeared in *The MacGuffin, The Evergreen Chronicles, The Madison Review,* and other publications. He teaches poetry to young people at the Juvenile Arts Corps of Pinellas. He also leads writing workshops for PWAs and the developmentally disabled. Timothy's first book of poems, *Between the Moon and One O'Clock,* will be published in the fall of 1998.

Hilarie Ayers, a graduating senior at California State University at Fullerton, characterizes her writing as "having a sly sense of humor and a fondness for S.A.T. quality words." Her poetry has been published in her high school yearbook, and as part of the Michael L. Roston Writing Contest.

Jonathan Vital recently graduated from the University of Pittsburgh with an M.F.A. in Creative Writing. He now lives in Philadelphia and plays drums in a band called The Low Numbers. In addition to short stories that have appeared in *Buckshot* and *Thaw,* Jonathan has written a novel titled *Enormous Hope.*

Marcy D. Olson lives and works in Marshall, Minnesota, where she studied creative writing, German, and philosophy at Southwest State University. She is co-founder and editor of the literary magazine *Bottomless Pot of Coffee*. Marcy holds a second-degree black belt in tae kwon do, and recently completed a children's nonfiction book on the sport. She is currently working on a book of short stories, a screenplay, and a collection of poems.

Barbara Egel works as a Qualitative Research Analyst in the Chicago area. Her other job (and joy) is her six-year-old daughter. Barbara's work has appeared in *Northeast Corridor*.

Jan Quackenbush was raised on a farm in the Endless Mountains region of northeast Pennsylvania. He still owns and maintains the farm. He is a professional playwright, whose works have been published and produced internationally. Jan has been married for twenty-five years, and has two children. He works at the Barnes & Noble store in Binghamton, New York.

Ramon C. Bautista was born in the Philippines and received his B.A. in English from the University of the Philippines. His work has appeared in *ZYZZYVA* and *Asian America*. Beginning in the fall of 1998, Ramon will attend graduate school in the Library Science program at St. John's University. He works in the Barnes & Noble store in Forest Hills, New York.

Adam Woodfill graduated from the Art Institute in Pittsburgh, Pennsylvaina, majoring in graphic design, before going on to study fiction writing at the University of Pittsburgh. His artwork, poems, and short stories have appeared in various magazines. Adam is the co-editor of the Pittsburgh-based literary journal *Buckshot.*

Mark Jared Zufelt is a poet and theater artist. His work has recently appeared in *Black Spring Review, Stovepipe Literary Journal, Mojo Risin'*, and *Lucid Moon.* A graduate of the National High School Institute of Theatre Arts at Northwestern University, and the Drama department at the University of California at Irvine, Mark has written, directed, and or performed in over thirty plays and films in the last ten years. A longtime resident of southern California, Mark now lives in Washington, D.C., and works at Arena Stage, where he has been awarded the Allen Lee Hughes Living Stage Fellowship for 1998-99.

Susan F. Bennett graduated from the University of Iowa's Playwright Workshop in 1989. She spent three years writing plays in New York City, then returned to her home state of Iowa to write fiction.

David Zapanta does not limit himself to writing poetry. He has written, illustrated, and self-published a comic book titled *Hairbat.* Currently going blind at his computer while working on his first novella, *Big Rush for Dumbville,* David resides in, as he puts it, "Manhattan proper."

Terry Endres teaches composition and literature courses at Cincinnati State College. As a freelance writer, he has published several articles on scientific curiosities and unusual phenomena. For fun, he enjoys reading, writing, adding to his Web site, strumming his guitar, or playing softball.

Terry lives in Cleves, Ohio, with his wife, Kim, and stepson, Clay.

Donna H. Murphy works full-time at Barnes & Noble. She is taking classes at the State University of New York at New Paltz, working toward a B.A. in English. Donna writes that although she "doesn't have any published work to boast of, being included in the anthology has encouraged me to continue writing, and to consider submitting more of my work for future publication."

Michael Odom, being a military brat, is from many places, but mostly places in California. At the time "Terzanelle" was written, he lived in Chico. By the time it was accepted for this anthology, he had moved to Orange County. Currently (depending on how far into the future "currently" is) he lives in San Francisco.

Brenn Jones is currently editing the *Barnes & Noble Guide to Children's Books,* to be published in 1999. He was born in London, England, and raised in Rochester, New York. Brenn studied at Swarthmore College and the University of Edinburgh. He lives on Manhattan's Lower East Side and spends his free time (when he's not searching for David Byrne) in Iceland.

Elizabeth Hansen is a sophomore Recording Industry major at Middle Tennessee State University in Murfreesboro. Originally from Smithville, Missouri, she is a member of the MTSU Films Committee, and a DJ on the student radio station, WMTS. Elizabeth is currently working on a series of essays about her concert experiences, as well as writing a novelty song about Jerry Springer. She has also contributed to The Haiku Haven, an Internet site devoted to haiku about everything from Spam to the Beastie Boys.

Rusty Barnes graduated from Mansfield University in Pennsylvania and Emerson College in Massachusetts. He lives in Boston with his wife, Heather Sullivan, and their daughter, Sierra.

Irene Polemis is a short story writer with an M.F.A. from Brooklyn College. She lives with her husband, Michael, in New Jersey on the cliffs of the Hudson River. "White Bundles: A Trilogy," the first section of which is published here, is part of a collage of short stories titled *Double Exposed.* The second section of "White Bundles," titled "Rocks," appeared in a recent issue of *The Paterson Literary Review.*

Stuart Miller was born in Paterson, New Jersey. He has an M.F.A. in Writing from the Columbia University School of the Arts. His poems and translations have appeared in a dozen magazines. In addition to *Between the Leaves*, Stuart has edited *Selected Poems of William Butler Yeats* and *Essays and Sketches of Mark Twain.* He is Editorial Director of Barnes & Noble Books, and lives in Brooklyn.

Linda E. Smit is currently an Assistant Manager at the new Barnes & Noble store in Hilton Head, South Carolina. She has written poetry since the age of three, but this is her first national publication. She has called everyone she knows to tell them about it.

Josh Niemand was living in Vermont at the time he submitted his work for this anthology. Since then, he has moved to New York City, where, like most New Yorkers, he spends his entire salary on rent. He will happily accept donations of food or money, as well as rockabilly, ska, and swing CDs.

Scott Nagele grew up in upstate New York. He is a graduate of Michigan State University, and currently resides in Okemos, Michigan. He writes after work, or whenever he can find the time. For the present, he is keeping his day job.

Joseph Gonnella, child of a librarian, has managed to spend most of his life with a book in his hands. He lives in Princeton Junction, New Jersey, with his wife, son, and a few thousand volumes organized by category and alphabetized by author. The section of "Sir Isaac Newton" included here is from a series in progress called *Lives*.

Todd Lazarus is Marketing Manager of the Barnes & Noble Merchandise Group. He lives in Manhattan.

Kris R. Davis is originally from Greensburg, Pennsylvania, but now lives in Folsom, California, at a safe distance from the many eligible bachelors who reside in the town's maximum security prison. She earned her B.A. in English Literature from San Francisco State University in 1995, and now divides her time between writing short stories and applying for numerous dead-end, minimum-wage jobs.

Cindy Dach has published her work in *Harper's, Seventeen,* and *The New Censorship*. She has also read her stories on KTCL and KHOW radio in Denver, Colorado. Cindy currently lives in Phoenix, Arizona, and has completed her first novel, *Conversations with the Weather*.

Erin Smith Hill has written and edited for magazines, including *San Diego Home/Garden Lifestyles* and *Engravers Journal.* A graduate student at the State Univeristy of New York at Buffalo, Erin plans to support herself as a school psychologist in the event that her dream position—world-renowned writer and coffee shop habitué—remains illusive. In either case, she will continue to write poetry and fiction. "Naked" is her first published poem.

Illustrators

Robin Yanes has been in the computer industry since 1986, and works as a senior database analyst in Westbury, New York. Before her current position, she was a nursery school teacher for several years. She is a graduate of Ohio State University.

Virginia Daggett grew up in Colorado and Kansas, and received her B.A. in Art Education from the University of Kansas. A former public school art teacher, Virginia has spent the last four years planning the "Crafts for Kids" story hour at the West Long Branch, New Jersey, Barnes & Noble store. Virginia and her husband, Ron, live in Red Bank, New Jersey. They have a son and a daughter.

Kourtney Harper was living and working in Chapel Hill, North Carolina, at the time she submitted her drawings for this anthology.

Chris Paradis is an artist, booklover, and student of esoteric wisdom and pop culture. He aspires to integrate the fire, water, air, and earth aspects of life to become an adept human being. Chris is currently doing all this in North Little Rock, Arkansas.

Larry Decker has been a freelance artist and illustrator since 1970. His work has appeared regularly in *National Parks & Conservation* magazine, *Farmstead* magazine, and various nature conservancy publications, as well as in *The New York Times*. Larry's paintings have been shown in a variety of galleries on Long Island and in upstate New York, and are currently being represented by the Jacob-Fanning Gallery in Wellfleet, Massachusetts. Larry manages the Barnes & Noble store in Colonie, New York, near Albany.